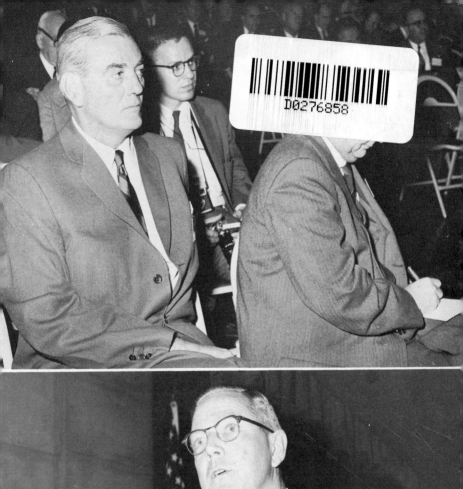

ENERGY
and MAN

A Symposium

14-120-1452

Allan Nevins
Robert G. Dunlop
Edward Teller
Edward S. Mason
Herbert Hoover, Jr.

with an Introduction by
Courtney C. Brown

ENERGY
and MAN

A Symposium

 Appleton-Century-Crofts, Inc.
New York

CONTENTS

ILLUSTRATIONS

Front Endpapers

Allan Nevins (*top left*); Edward Teller (*bottom left*); Herbert Hoover, Jr., and Courtney C. Brown (*top right*); Robert Dunlop (*bottom right*).

Back Endpapers

Herbert Hoover, Jr., Edward S. Mason, and Robert Dunlop (standing), Grayson Kirk, President of Columbia University, Frank M. Porter, President of the American Petroleum Institute, Courtney C. Brown, and Allan Nevins (sitting) (*top left*); Herbert Hoover, Jr. (*bottom left*); Edward S. Mason (*top right*); Courtney C. Brown speaking, Frank M. Porter, Edward Teller, Edward S. Mason, and Herbert Hoover, Jr., listening (*bottom right*).

INTRODUCTION

THROUGH THE AGES, LEARNING HAS LOOKED TO THE WORLD of practical affairs for the major subjects of its interest. It is very appropriate that a great university, Columbia, through its Graduate School of Business, should share with a great industry, through its representative, the American Petroleum Institute, an inquiry into the role of energy, past, present, and future, in the lives of each of us.

Another name for energy is prime mover. The world most certainly is on the move, not just physically, but culturally, politically, and in other ways. The availability of an abundant and inexpensive supply of energy should condition the direction of these moves perhaps more than any other factor. Just as the successive harnessing of prime movers in the past in the form of animal power, wind power, water power, and now mineral power has changed the cultural, political, and physical scene in which life occurs, so will the forms and abundance of the energy supplies of tomorrow condition the milieu in which we live.

So, when early in 1959 the American Petroleum Institute asked the Graduate School of Business if it would collaborate in the preparation and presentation of a comprehensive symposium worthy to serve as a part of the commemoration of the centennial of the oil business in the United States, we were delighted to accept. It was decided that it would be appropriate to consider energy in its several forms and to discuss circumstances that will best assure its continued availability in abundance. Thus, on November 4, 1959, a group of over three hundred government officials, economists, historians, scientists, and executives from a broad range of industry gathered in the rotunda of Columbia's Low Memorial Library to hear delivered and to discuss the papers which are reprinted in this volume.

In introducing this inquiry into energy and its impact on our lives, a brief word should be said about the program's "grand" design, as well as about each of the speakers. The presentations start with an account of the role of energy in the history of Western man by Dr. Allan Nevins. It would be redundant to plunge into an extended introduction of Dr. Nevins. Suffice it to say he is one of the country's leading historians, a man whose insights, particularly into the past of the American scene, have provided us all with stimulation and enlightenment. Dr. Nevins is on familiar ground when he speaks from a Columbia platform. The recipient of two Pulitzer Prizes for work in history and biography, he has presented a number of classic interpretations of the early history of the petroleum business.

Building on this background, the program moves to a discussion by Mr. Robert Dunlop of petroleum's impact over the last century as a major source of energy, or prime mover. The only representative of the petroleum industry on the program, Mr. Dunlop has been President of the Sun Oil Company for the last twelve years. He is regarded as one of the best informed authorities in the oil business on the economics of the industry and has been active in seeking effective presentations of public affairs issues affecting it. He is a director of the American Petroleum Institute and serves as a trustee of the University of Pennsylvania.

Mr. Dunlop's paper is followed by a survey of the future —of those energy sources that are now in the laboratory or pilot plants, but promise to have profound influence in the years to come. The speaker, Dr. Edward Teller, is Professor of Physics at the University of California and Director of the Radiation Laboratory at Livermore, California. Born in Budapest, Hungary, and educated in Germany, Dr. Teller came to this country in 1935 to teach at George Washington University. Shortly after the start of World War II, he was assigned to the Manhattan Project and during the next few years he rendered outstanding service to his adopted country. Dr. Teller has made important contributions in the fields of electric and nuclear physics, and in quantum theory. In recent years he has been noted for his work on the practical applications of thermonuclear principles and the development of thermonuclear weapons.

Next in sequence comes an analysis of some of the conditions—political, physical, and economic—that will be necessary to assure an abundant supply of low-cost energy, presented by Dr. Edward S. Mason. A member of the Harvard faculty since 1923, Dr. Mason was Dean of the Harvard Graduate School of Public Administration from 1947 to 1958, when he chose to become Frank W. Taussig Professor of Economics and to devote his full time to teaching and research. During World War II, he served as Chief Economist for the Office of Strategic Services and was Deputy to the Assistant Secretary of State. He was Chief Economic Advisor to the United States at the Moscow Conference in 1947, and in 1954–55 he directed the team which assisted in drawing up a plan for the economic development of Pakistan.

The program concludes with a paper by Mr. Herbert Hoover, Jr., on energy and public affairs which provides a broad view of the energy story against a world-wide background. A consulting engineer by profession, Mr. Hoover has worked with a number of firms in the United States and abroad, besides acting as a consultant to the governments of Venezuela, Iran, Brazil, Peru, and other nations. In 1953 he was a special advisor on world-wide petroleum matters to the Secretary of State, and he served as Under Secretary of State from 1954 to 1957.

It was a particularly great privilege for the Graduate School of Business of Columbia University to share in this occasion. The proceedings were tape-recorded by the Voice of America, and the publication of these distinguished lectures will constitute, I believe, a fitting document to commemorate this important birthday of a great and dynamic industry.

Thanks are due to Mr. Frank M. Porter, President of the

American Petroleum Institute, who presided over the afternoon session, and to the staff of that organization for their efficient help in preparing for the occasion. I would like also to acknowledge the assistance of Professor William A. Owens of Columbia University, the author of *Fever in the Earth,* a recent novel about petroleum, who was responsible for preparing the lectures for publication.

COURTNEY C. BROWN
Dean, Graduate School of Business
Columbia University

I.   ENERGY IN THE HISTORY OF WESTERN MAN

by Allan Nevins

WHEN, JUST OVER A CENTURY AGO—TO BE EXACT, ON AUGUST 21, 1859—Colonel E. L. Drake made himself the Aladdin of petroleum, a nation hungry for energy unconsciously waited on his discovery. How hungry it was may be gathered from the fact that the engine which sank his 69½-foot shaft at the rate of three feet a day had barely six horse-power; and that one of the first wells driven by an imitator, James Evans the blacksmith, was "kicked down" by man-power.

It requires an effort of the imagination to carry us back to the corner of Pennsylvania and the primitive industrial world in which this discovery took place. By that effort, we can picture to ourselves the Pittsburgh of 1859, a grimy, boisterous town of coal miners, ironworkers, farmers, steam-boatmen, and emigrants, its street crowded with carts and omnibuses, its sky tawny with smoke. We can picture the rough country stretching north from Pittsburgh to Lake Erie, green, wild, and empty. Through it run the blue waters of the Allegheny River; its margins becoming rockier and its current swifter as we look up to the abrupt hills and unhewn forests of northwestern Pennsylvania. Only a cen-

3

tury earlier Britain and France were battling for mastery of this unmapped region between the Lakes and the head-waters of the Ohio. Ill-mapped it was still in 1859; for the main bodies of frontiersmen, roadbuilders, and settlers had swept by on the east-west waterways, leaving this area little touched. The upper Allegheny was yet a wilderness river, floating down rafts of timber; its tributary creeks threaded narrow valleys with poor marginal farms and shabby vil-lages of obscure name—Titusville, Meadville, Tidioute. In some of these creeks patches of oil stained the water, but nobody had thought of these patches as energy.

Then came one of the most startling transformations in American annals. The wondering cry of "Oil! Oil!" raised by the young son of Drake's helper was a spark falling on a charge of explosive. The region filled with shouting men, long lines of straining teams and wagons, derricks and engine houses, hotels and saloons. Even amid the clangor of the Civil War it was a national marvel; and before that conflict ended petroleum vied with the grains of the Missis-sippi Valley in earning European gold for the hard-pressed country.

Throughout history, mankind in its incessant search for energy has been haunted by a fear of shortages and ultimate exhaustion. Indeed, this spectral fear must run back to pre-history. No doubt the most intelligent Neolithic tribesmen, looking at the woods that gave them fuel and the aurochs that supplied meat and fat, sometimes ruminated: "What will happen when they are gone?" One of the most inter-esting chapters of George P. Marsh's once-famous book, *The Earth as Modified by Human Action,* is entitled "The

4

Destructiveness of Man," and treats of the scarcities of energy, in various forms, which man wantonly created. This apprehensive attitude can be traced down to our modern literature on the balance between natural resource and human population; it inspired Malthus, and troubled Aldous Huxley. Balzac's apocalyptic novel, *The Wild Ass's Skin*, may be regarded as a double allegory. This story of a young man who owns a magic piece of hide which grants him every wish, but which shrinks every time the wish is granted, expounds the law that every individual excess extracts its price. But its significance might be widened to expound the law that mankind pays a collective price for its extravagances. Balzac's hero was startled, after one orgy, to observe how terribly his magic piece of skin had shrunk; just so, Americans were startled, after the two World Wars, to note how those global orgies of hate and waste had depleted some of our irreplaceable resources.

Yet from age to age these historic fears have been proved false. This is partly because of the repeated discovery by man of such new stores of natural energy as Drake's well disclosed. It is interesting to note that European journals today are discussing the prospects of a world energy surplus in the immediate future. Coal stocks on the Continent and in the United Kingdom have lately totalled eighty million tons, and Poland and the Soviet Union have been making earnest efforts to find European outlets for their coal. Still more impressive are the indications of a great augmentation in the flow of petroleum. Information given at the recent Fifth Annual Petroleum Congress indicates that the industry now anticipates a decade of oil surplus. Discoveries of

5

petroleum have been made in the last few years at the rate of about thirty-three billion barrels annually, and world oil reserves—the wild ass's skin in this field of energy—are computed to offer a supply, at the present rate of consumption, for forty-two years. New discoveries will be made. While more than two-thirds of the present known reserves are in the Middle East, the finding of oil and gas in Libya and the Sahara, in West Africa and France, in Italy and Canada, promises to shatter the present picture.

The release of new stores of energy has also been keyed throughout history to mechanical invention; a truth so obvious for nearly all of man's known past that we are tempted to think of invention as the master key of energy. By far the greatest part of the human record is a chronicle of mere muscle power, exerted by men or draft animals. If windmills existed anywhere before the eleventh century, they were rare and primitive. Any effective use of the water mill, historically speaking, is as recent. All those who have studied the past from the standpoint of economics, and those especially who have studied economic geography, are aware that from the material point of view, history is primarily the story of the increasing ability of man to reach and control energy. In the endless centuries when energy meant muscle power alone, how great an advance was the invention of the wheel, a device known to the ancient East, but one beyond the reach of the Aztec and Inca cultures. How great an advance, again, was registered by man when in 312 B.C. the Romans commenced the building of the Appian Way, almost the oldest and certainly the grandest of the roads with which they checkered Western Europe. The inventors of wheel, road, and fulcrum carried the age of mere muscle as far as it could go; the men who, by the sail, the windmill, and the water wheel harnessed those uncertain, treacherous helpers, the air and the stream, took but a short step beyond.

Looking back on the centuries of muscle power, and marveling at the pyramids, the walled palaces and cities, and the canals built by sheer animal energy, we easily ignore or forget the appalling limitations and hardships, the heartbreaking agonies, entailed by man's ignorance of the stores of energy about him and of the means of utilizing them. We readily falsify the basic situation. John Masefield's well-known poem "Cargoes," which from one point of view offers a contrast in cultures, and from another standpoint a contrast in the use of energy, is an apt illustration of this fact. We all recall its vivid lines. "Quinquireme of Nineveh from distant Ophir," it runs, "Rowing home to haven in sunny Palestine"—

> With a cargo of ivory,
> And apes and peacocks,
> Sandalwood, cedarwood, and sweet white wine.

And against this it sets the contrast of "Dirty British coaster with a salt-caked smokestack, butting through the Channel in the mad March days"—

> With a cargo of Tyne coal,
> Road-rails, pig-lead,
> Firewood, ironware, and cheap tin trays.[1]

[1] From *Collected Poems* by John Masefield, © 1951 by John Masefield, and used by permission of The Macmillan Co.

The superficial reader might prefer the ivory, apes, and peacocks. But that was not Masefield's intent. The reader need only ask himself which lot he would rather have, that of the galley slave manning his heavy oar under a burning sun and a stinging lash, or that of a seaman letting the sturdy engine of the modern freighter push his craft through the North Sea chop.

Nor need we turn to Nineveh for slave labor; one hundred years ago America herself had slaves, four million of them, whose toil furnished no inconsiderable part of the national energy. They have been liberated in more senses than one. "A century after Colonel Drake's discovery," states the Atlantic Refining Company, "only one per cent of America's physical work is done by man himself. The rest is done by machines, and petroleum provides more than 70 per cent of the energy that activates those machines."[1]

As in the symbolic figure of Colonel Drake we honor those who have uncovered new reserves of energy, so we should never cease to honor the men who have led the way, by mechanical invention, in its more efficient application. Doubtless the greatest single revolution in the history of applied energy dates from the hour when, at the beginning of the eighteenth century, a mechanic of Devonshire, employed as an ironmonger, became interested in the experiments of two or three older men in the use of steam as primary power. The mechanic was named Thomas Newcomen. The Britain about him faced an exigent problem. Coal was increasingly needed for heating houses, for the forge of the blacksmith, for the kiln of the limeburner, for the furnace

[1] Used by permission of the Atlantic Refining Company.

of the lead smelter. Miners were driving their shafts deeper and deeper; and water had to be pumped from them in such enormous quantities that some collieries kept 250 or 300 horses to drive the pumps. The expense of the stables was enormous; muscle had gone as far as it could go. Already another ingenious mechanic, one Thomas Savery, had invented a means of lifting water from the mines; not an engine, but a device by which the sudden condensation of hot steam in an iron chamber created a vacuum, which raised water from the shafts. This device had no moving parts; it was slow and cumbrous, and Newcomen took a long step forward—one of the longest steps in history.

He invented a cylinder which enclosed a piston, and he applied Savery's principle of a vacuum in the wake of condensing steam to this new contrivance. That is, he projected the steam against the piston, forcing it upward; he then, by using a spray of cold water to condense the steam, created a vacuum which drew the piston down; and this reciprocating action of the piston produced pumping energy. His feat of the year 1712 was an event beside which Marlborough's victories pale into insignificance. Mankind could turn its face from the muscle energy of horses, elephants, slaves, and servants, from the windmills of Don Quixote's Spain and the water mills of a thousand streams. Before Newcomen died in 1729 he had built twenty engines, his invention was pumping water from nearly all the large mines of Britain, and its fame was spreading to other lands.

Then came James Smeaton, who built a steam engine to take the place of such windmills as had long drained the lowlands of Holland and Lincolnshire. His engine was re-

9

garded as gigantic; its steam cylinder had a diameter of fifty-two inches, and its piston a stroke of nine feet. After him came a man of genius, the instrument-maker James Watt, whom the University of Glasgow hired to repair one of Newcomen's engines. He at once perceived its principal defect. It wasted, as Smeaton had calculated, more than 99 per cent of the energy produced by its fuel. This was primarily because the cylinder was alternately heated by scalding steam and chilled by cold water to condense it. Watt made the condenser a separate part; the cylinder could remain hot. He also added machinery to produce two power strokes on each revolution instead of one, and a revolving shaft which made it easy to gear the engines to other purposes than pumping. The age of steam had arrived; the age in which a Boulton & Watt engine was soon giving energy to factories, and driving Fulton's *Clermont* on its historic voyage up the Hudson.

At the very beginning a historic incident illustrated the fact that the new advance would add to human leisure as well as human wealth. When Newcomen's first engine was put to work, a boy was hired to turn on the jet of water at the end of each piston stroke to condense the steam. This lad, Humphrey Potter, found the job specially irksome because he owned a new fishing rod. It occurred to him that he might attach two cords from the rocking-beam to the water faucet. As the piston went up, one cord opened the faucet; as it went down, the other cord closed it. Two other cords opened and closed the steam cock. Seeing that his innovation worked better than human power, Humphrey slipped away to the nearest trout stream. What a pity, Mr.

LeGrand Skinner of the Skinner Engine Works observed to the Newcomen Society of America a few years ago, that we do not know how many fish he caught! But in his concept of a self-acting steam engine he had already landed a fish of the largest magnitude.

Yet neither the Newcomens nor the Drakes touched the true fountainhead of energy. While men were making windmills, mining coal, devising steam engines, ushering in the industrial revolution, and striking oil to speed it, an entirely different set of workers, actuated by quite another body of motives, was opening the true source. They were not concerned with raising water from Dutch polders, with putting electric currents to work, or making internal combustion engines. Most of them were utterly impractical. In the end, however, they were to harness energies far excelling any at the command of the prospector or mechanical inventor.

The story of the real openers of the fountainhead of energy might well begin in the thirteenth century with the Sicilian court of the Hohenstaufen head of the Holy Roman Empire, Frederick II. He was a monarch of insatiable curiosity. He knew six languages, was versed in mathematics, philosophy, and biology, and took a keen interest in medicine, patronizing the great school at Salerno. He was eminent as a lawgiver. But it was his concern with the discovery of scientific truth—pure truth for its own sake—which makes him immortally interesting. The Emperor Frederick converted his court in Norman Sicily into a meeting place of Greek, Latin, Arabic, and Germanic cultures. He welcomed there the most eminent scientific thinkers whom he could find. One was Michael Scott, born in Scotland,

11

schooled in Spain, traveled in all Europe; a cosmopolite, humanist, and research worker of vast renown. He knew Arabian astronomy, he translated Avicenna's book *De Animalibus*, and he was proud of his accuracy in scientific observations and mathematical calculations. Another scholar at the court was Master Theodore, the philosopher who came to Sicily from the Great Caliph in Cairo; himself Greek or Jewish, he brought a fund of Eastern lore in mathematics, hygiene, and astrology. Still another member of the circle was Leonard of Pisa, forever famous as the man who introduced Arabic numerals and algebra to the West.

The experimentalism in science encouraged by Frederick II included some activities of which modern inquirers would hardly approve. He shut up one man in a wine cask, it is related, to test the Epicurean doctrine that the soul dies with the body. He disemboweled two men in order to compare the effects of sleep and of exercise upon digestion. He caused some children to be reared in utter silence to ascertain whether they would first speak Hebrew, the supposed parent of languages, or Greek, or Arabic; alas, they all died before they spoke anything. But in founding the University of Naples and supporting the school at Salerno; in encouraging a large group of scientists to labor for abstract truth and nothing else; in corresponding with other monarchs to assemble scientific data; in collecting the greatest animal zoo of his time; and in putting to scholars some searching inquiries which became renowned as "the Sicilian questions," he set in motion impulses of wide influence. He laid before the eminent Jewish scholar of Toledo, Jehuda ben Solomon Cohen, a striking series of geometrical problems.

Through the Sultan of Egypt, he requested Moslem scholars to send him solutions of knotty problems in optics—one being, "Why do objects partly covered by water appear bent?" In short, his life gave new impetus to the human intellect.

Some of the Sicilian questions would strike many readers of today as silly; so true it is that, as Macaulay once wrote, men are slow to comprehend that truth grows first the tiny blade, then the empty ear, then the full corn in the ear. I saw recently a set of modern Sicilian questions, the interrogatives that a present-day Frederick would ask. "What is matter?" runs one of them. "How can it be both discrete particles, and continuous wave patterns of energy?" For another, "What holds the nucleus together?" For a third, "What is the source of cosmic rays, those mysterious high-energy particles?" For a fourth, "Why are galaxies spiral?" A fifth question runs: "What is the secret of the synthesis of protoplasm?" And finally, we find a query which should interest the conductors of quiz programs on radio: "Just what is memory?" May men, in the progress of knowledge, come to deem these problems absurdly simple too!

Frederick II died in 1250; the Holy Roman Empire entered on its long decay; and in time, after harrowing turmoil, a new age dawned. This modern age presently gave birth to what Alfred North Whitehead has called the century of genius—the seventeenth century. He gave it that label because he recalled that Newton was born in the year that Galileo died, 1642, and just as Descartes published his *Meditationes* and *Principia Philosophiae*. Within that century fall the great names of Francis Bacon, who opened it with his *Advancement of Learning* (1605), Kepler, Galileo, Harvey, Descartes, Pascal, Huyghens, Boyle, Newton, Locke, Spinoza, and Leibnitz—to give only twelve names when scores might be noted. What made this efflorescence of scientific genius possible?

Of the many factors involved, one of the chief was assuredly the shattering of the old theological modes of thought, and the rise of a new rationalism, a belief that the primary road to truth lay through an analysis of the nature of things. One was a rising sense of the detailed complexity of the order of nature. Still another element was the emergence of a superior mathematics, adequate to the analysis of vibratory phenomena. But the greatest factor of all, I think, was this: the development of society to a point at which large numbers of talented men could devote themselves, in numerous parts of Europe, to pure thought and pure scientific inquiry; where they had seats of learning, laboratories, command of leisure, and respect; and where they were free to publish the results of their thinking—for as Galileo died, and Newton was born, John Milton was about to publish his *Areopagitica.*

These men struck the fountainhead of energy with hardly a thought of its practical applications and none at all of its pecuniary possibilities. The poor German, Johann Kepler, in a life full of misfortune, succeeded by sheer genius, despite defective eyesight, in placing astronomy on an entirely new foundation. The yet greater Italian, Galileo, son of a decayed Florentine nobleman, helped make mechanics a science and vastly expanded the bounds of the universe by his telescopic observations and illumined nu-

merous physical problems by his happy mastery of mathematical analysis. Both were great, and both in the long
development of knowledge did a fertile work in enlarging
our mastery of energy, because they pursued pure science
and it alone. It is certain that Kepler, beyond drawing some
astrological horoscopes for which he apologized on the
ground of necessity, never thought of practical applications.
Galileo's type of telescopic instrument is embodied in the
modern opera glass; he improved the microscope when it
was a new invention; and he formulated the rules by which
the pendulum could be employed to regulate clocks, though
he left it to Huyghens to apply the principle effectively. But
in his passionate search for truth he never took thought for
utilitarian ends, and the lack of "practical results" would
never have troubled him even had he not enjoyed a sinecure
which honored the Italy of his day.

So it was with the other great immortals of science. Sir
Isaac Newton was responsible for a many-sided and inspired body of work on light, color, and optics. He discovered the binomial theorem. He formulated for his own
time, and in great part for all time, the basic laws of mechanics. He performed many other labors. It is probably
just to say that he did more to unlock the secrets of energy
in the universe than any predecessor, and he opened the
way for further discoveries of direct practical importance.
Yet he was an essentially unworldly man, and the cost of
publishing his *Principia* was defrayed by his friend Halley.
Michael Faraday, the poor son of a blacksmith, was inspired
with a passion to learn chemistry by a lecture delivered by
Sir Humphrey Davy at the Royal Institution. He was soon

15

Davy's assistant. Turning to electricity, he devised in 1831 the first electric generator, the dynamo which Henry Adams thought a fitting emblem of modern civilization; he first analyzed the suitability of different substances for electrical induction; and he laid down the law of electrolytic phenomena. Upon his discoveries were eventually founded a host of practical applications of electrical energy. To all this, however, he was indifferent. His mission in life, carried out in the Royal Institution, was the discovery of truth; others could make the applications.

Another illustration of the same attitude is provided by the Russian scientist Mendeleev, whose career should teach us much concerning the respect in which our chief rival in world affairs has long held pure science. When Mendeleev came on the scientific scene as a teacher in the St. Petersburg technological institute, during our Civil War, the atom was generally regarded as an ultimate entity. Matter could not be broken down into more infinitesimal elements; science could study the relations among atoms, but not probe within them. His laborious establishment of the Periodic Law, by which elements ranged according to the magnitude of atomic weights show a periodic change of properties, did much to create an entirely new conception of the atom. His law proved potent in classifying the elements, in predicting the existence and nature of elements yet unknown, in determining correct atomic weights, and in inspiring scientists to study the internal structure of atoms. Inquiry turned to the nature of electrons within the atom; by a momentous step the New Zealander Ernest Rutherford split the atom; and the sequels in the disclosure of an incalculably powerful source of energy are vaguely known to, if not understood by, the whole world.

Mendeleev is of particular interest to us because of his concern with petroleum. When he visited the United States in the centennial year 1876, he hastened to the oil regions of Pennsylvania to study the wells, and to the refineries of Philadelphia to examine their techniques. He wrote a report which he hoped would be useful in the development of the oil resources of Baku and the Caucasus. Even in this area, however, his interest was not primarily utilitarian, for it was on the origin and nature of petroleum that he focused his attention. First a teacher in the University of St. Petersburg and later a director of a scientific bureau in the government, he gave his life to the advancement of pure science.

Shortly after Dr. Abraham Flexner persuaded Einstein to take a research chair in the Institute for Advanced Study at Princeton, he published a plea for widening the type of opportunity for abstract scientific work that he was giving the author of the theory of relativity. It was a plea, he said, for less emphasis on the word "use," and more emphasis on the freeing of the human spirit. "To be sure," he explained, "we shall thus waste some precious dollars, but what is infinitely more important is the fact that we shall be striking off the shackles of the human mind and setting it free for the adventures which in our own day have taken Hale and Rutherford and Einstein and their peers millions upon millions of miles into the uttermost realms of space, and released the boundless energy imprisoned in the atom. What Rutherford and others like Bohr and Millikan have done out of sheer curiosity in the effort to understand the construction of the atom has released forces which may transform human life; but this ultimate, unforeseen, and unpredictable practical result is not offered as a plea in justification of their careers." What Dr. Flexner termed curiosity I would call passion for exact truth; a quest for truth regardless of its immediate utility or inutility, undertaken in the confident belief that pure science will ultimately serve humanity even better than Watt and Stephenson, Edison and Marconi, Diesel and Westinghouse, served it.

Where are the real, the final fountainheads of energy? We, standing in the major universities of the land, amid laboratories and libraries, and almost within earshot of our cyclotrons, can say: "Here! Here are the men and agencies that will in the long run do most to reach the fountainheads." The plea for enlarged comprehension of this fact gains urgency. Not long ago the Atlantic Congress appointed a subcommittee on scientific and technical co-operation under NATO, composed of thirty distinguished men from ten NATO countries. Their report has just been published. The chief conclusions are four, which in my own language run as follows. First, the imminence of fierce economic competition from our opponents now forces us to re-examine the Free World's industrial foundations; its foundations of energy. Second, the growth potential of any economy is determined by its technological base, which in turn is determined by its scientific foundation; and the Atlantic Community cannot succeed unless it expands its scientific base in systematic fashion. Third, the footing of basic scientific research is found in the universities, and in the laboratories of industry, government, and special scientific institutions. "All this, in turn, is grounded on the bedrock of education; education in science and engineering which recognizes that the humanities, too, are indispensable in the balance and discipline of accomplished minds."[1] Finally, the new effort should be broadly international, and it would be well to found at least a few universities which would draw their faculties and students broadly from the whole Atlantic Community.

The history of the United States is the history of optimism and progress; it has not been so clearly the history of organized and purposeful effort; it has been still less the history of Spartan dedication to great and difficult goals. We must believe that we can and will succeed; but we cannot succeed without discipline, self-denial, and vision. We have been efficiently pragmatic but we must remember that immediate utility is not enough. We should have a civilization favorable to the spirit which animated Galileo in the University of Padua, Newton in Cambridge, Helmholtz in Heidelberg and Berlin, and Niels Bohr in Copenhagen. The energy represented by coal seams and oil pools is limited; here the magic piece of wild ass's skin will indeed shrink. But as the quest of pure science is endless, so the results it may bring, the vistas it may open, are infinite. Dr. Flexner took me once to spend a Saturday afternoon with Einstein. In the course of our talk, I happened to recall the familiar remark of Newton at the end of his life that, looking back,

[1] From *On Increasing the Effectiveness of Western Science and Technology*, report of the Rapporteur Robert McKinney to the Subcommittee on Scientific and Technical Co-operation, Atlantic Congress, London, 1959. Used by permission.

he could see that he had been only a child wandering on the shores of science, picking up a bright pebble here and there, while the boundless ocean of truth rolled all unplumbed beside him. The quotation for all its triteness fired Einstein. "Yes," he said with sudden fervor. "And that was not just a poetic image. Newton meant it precisely, every word." He implied that he too had been a childlike wanderer on the same shore. So it will ever be; while oil burns, dynamos whir, and machinery serves us all, the truest creators of energy will be those who have the higher fervor—who ask only for an opportunity to search the shore for more bright pebbles, to catch new gleams from the ocean of truth.

DEAN BROWN: Thank you, Professor Nevins. It has been said that man's chief resource is his own resourcefulness. This remarkably succinct account of the resourcefulness of those who have gone before us in the field of energy indeed throws the challenge to us of today, as well as to those in the years ahead.

Now, to start the discussion, I would like to ask Professor Nevins the first question. In your talk, you referred interestingly but rather briefly to the relationship between inquiry regarding energy and the development of the usefulness of energy and the wheel. We have all heard a great deal in recent years of new ways of using energy that do not involve the wheel, whether it be jet propulsion, surface propulsion on an air cushion, or propulsion on a track. Is there, in your judgment, Professor Nevins, a relationship between the amount of mental energy that we put to the further development of physical energy and the ways in which we find to use it?

DR. NEVINS: These attempts to eliminate the wheel are, of course, attempts to reduce friction. This reminds us that mankind for a long time pursued the idea of perpetual motion, and that the impossibility of creating a device for perpetual motion was first conclusively demonstrated by those who ascertained the law of conservation of energy. Once that was expounded and published abroad, it was evident that perpetual motion was a dream. We can never quite eliminate friction, mechanical or mental. What I was trying to present this morning was a plea for the endowment and encouragement of more mental friction in an effort to reduce more physical friction, or to evade it.

DEAN BROWN: Thank you. I have another question here that it seems particularly appropriate for an academic administrator to ask. Is state support of scholars the correct way to unbind Prometheus?

DR. NEVINS: That is, of course, a very interesting question. I'm happy to say that on that matter I find myself in harmony with John Stuart Mill. One could ask for no better support. John Stuart Mill said that elementary, secondary, and higher education was best supported by the combined energy of the church, the state, and private benefactions. All three are needed. No one should have a monopoly, and a balance among the three is highly salutary. Does that answer your question?

DEAN BROWN: I think we have a pretty good balance at present in this country.

DR. NEVINS: Yes, in the support of higher education, the

churches, the industries, the great benefactors, and the state are all active. All are needed.

DEAN BROWN: I think you will agree, Professor, that although they're in good balance, there should be more of all.

DR. NEVINS: Yes, there should be more of all.

DEAN BROWN: Another question. Professor Nevins, you assume great waste of oil in wartime. Eugene Ayres, in *Energy Sources, the Wealth of the World*—and then there's a commercial thrown in here, McGraw-Hill, 1952—says the facts do not support such assumptions. Will you elaborate? On the question of the great waste of energy in a period of war, particularly World War II.

DR. NEVINS: In speaking of the terrible waste of energy in two World Wars, I was thinking of the whole range of our natural reserves, including copper, lead, tin, zinc, and all the rest of our resources, needed in any development of our energy. While there has not been, may not have been, a highly visible waste of our petroleum resources, there certainly has been some waste of them in war. There are many commodities in our national cupboard which are much scarcer than petroleum, particularly when you consider that ultimately coal may even be convertible into petroleum. They were manifestly depleted by the two World Wars. There the skin of the ass did shrink. And I think this was pointed out with great energy after the Second World War. Natural resources had been reduced to a danger point in some areas. We can't afford these orgies of waste and hate, as I called them.

DEAN BROWN: Thank you very much, Professor Nevins.

II. THE PETROLEUM REVOLUTION

by Robert G. Dunlop

DEAN BROWN, DR. NEVINS, DISTINGUISHED GUESTS, LADIES
and gentlemen: John Fischer, Editor of *Harper's Magazine,*
wrote an article this summer for the special Centennial edi-
tion of the American Petroleum Institute *Quarterly.* In his
article, he points out that many petroleum products reach
us in strange disguises—"as a plastic grocery bag, for example, or a stocking on a pretty ankle." Other petroleum
products are seldom seen, even when undisguised. As Mr.
Fischer admits, "Though my home has been heated by fuel
oil for many years, to this day I have no idea what it looks
like." Black? he asks, or yellow? or water-clear? He adds
that only through the carelessness of a service station at-
tendant has he ever seen a splash of gasoline, and here I
don't know whether to say I hope it proved to be blue or not.

Mr. Fischer's experience is typical, yet to most Americans
the term "petroleum revolution" does not introduce an un-
familiar idea. The changes brought about by petroleum,
seen or unseen, are in fact so enormous that I believed it
impossible to speak on "The Petroleum Revolution" in the
space of some thirty-five minutes. Then it struck me that

25

Professor Nevins had been asked to cover, in thirty-five minutes, the impact of energy of all kinds on the whole history and culture of Western man! Earlier I had great admiration for his courage; having now heard him speak, my great admiration for his ability is well confirmed. I am honored to share this platform with him, and with the distinguished gentlemen who will follow on this program.

Moreover, I am proud, as I am sure all oil men and women are, that these outstanding Americans, and so great an institution as Columbia University, should lend their names and expend their energies on behalf of a Centennial Symposium in recognition of the hundredth birthday of our industry.

It pleases me to note that on its hundredth birthday, the petroleum industry is not a tired, old industry. The petroleum revolution is not history, but is a current, pulsating event, still unfolding. Furthermore, it would be inadequate to regard the petroleum revolution solely in terms of a vast expansion of available energy, although such indeed is one of its major characteristics.

The writer of a *Newsweek* roundup a few months ago may have been given to lyricism when he said: "The whole bountiful civilization of the mid-twentieth century is petroleum and the myriad economic and scientific reactions it has stimulated or helped to make possible."[1] But as an oil man, with pride that may be pardonable, I am inclined to say he was only moderately lyrical. For oil men did much more than drill wells and proclaim: "Look we have found

[1] From "Spotlight on Business," *Newsweek*, June 1, 1959. Used by permission.

petroleum. There is much of it. It is cheap. Come get some."

Under the thrust of competition, which was midwife at its birth, petroleum developed as an industry of great independence and vitality, as a restless innovator which continuously shook up the status quo. Its momentum started chain reactions extending into the technologies of other industries as well as directly into the everyday living of everyday Americans. To say that the industry was bent upon finding profitable markets for the rising tide of crude oil and natural gas it had learned how to find and produce, is to say that it was bent upon turning its discoveries into products increasingly useful and appealing to people, and serving them wherever they might be.

How well it has succeeded may be measured, at least partially, by the extent to which petroleum supplies the nation's energy requirement. Today, some 70 per cent of the energy we consume in the United States comes from crude oil and natural gas. Using such a number to highlight the significance of the petroleum revolution is handy, but it is also grossly inexact. It does not even fully encompass the explosive effect on the economy of the mobility provided by the gasoline engine. Moreover, where are the numbers that measure the significance of a carefully engineered lubrication system for, let's say, high-speed machine tools powered by electricity generated from coal? Or the significance of the creation of whole new industries, some based on new raw materials from petroleum, and others based on the petroleum industry's pressure for new or improved tools and materials? What I wish to suggest is that petroleum is

27

more than a source of energy, and that the petroleum revolution springs not just from the remarkable versatility of the hydrocarbon, but also from the dynamic nature of the industry itself.

Insight into the nature and characteristics of the petroleum industry may be gained by considering the circumstances of its birth and the physical form of its raw materials and products. One outstanding fact is that the industry was born at the right time; it had almost unlimited opportunities for speedy growth. At the time Edwin L. Drake's historic well came in, improvements in education and communication were creating a rising market for illuminants, while the oceans seemed to be running out of whales, drying up the source of the most widely used lamp oils. Techniques for distilling both coal and oil had been worked out, and crude oil proved to be an advantageous raw material for the fairly substantial coal oil refineries already in operation. Progress in mechanization offered a great opportunity for anyone who came along with more satisfactory lubricants. The groundwork had been laid for the coming of the automobile; for example, rubber had been vulcanized, the laws of magnetoelectric induction had been developed, thermodynamics was emerging as a science, even a differential for road vehicles had been invented. On top of everything else, free enterprise was coming into flower and incentives were strong. The country was operating full blast on the concept that talent is where God has put it, and the best way to bring it out is to give every man an opportunity to venture. There were plenty who welcomed the opportunity.

In its fourth annual report, the New York State Chamber of Commerce noted the export from the Port of New York of one million five hundred thousand gallons of petroleum products in the first three months of 1862—a bare two and a half years after Drake's well came in. "No article of commerce," the report noted, "has in so short a period of time ever made such rapid strides into the first ranks of valuable earth products as this."

To those who were alert to business affairs at that time, it seemed as though the petroleum industry had sprung up overnight. This, of course, was a consequence not only of demand, but of supply as well, and in this connection a second outstanding fact is that petroleum arrived in particularly fortunate forms. The migratory nature of petroleum is a function of those forms. Migration, plus the law of capture, placed great competitive pressure on the oil man to produce. He could not safely "sit on" his reserves, awaiting more favorable climes, for his oil or gas would find its way to someone else's well. Once produced, petroleum could not easily be stored—piled up on a vacant lot like coal or wood—so again, because of its physical form, the oil man was under great competitive pressure to sell. For the same reason, petroleum presented unique problems in transportation and distribution, an adversity which created competitive pressures leading to technological and economic consequences of great importance. As just one example, there are today more miles of pipelines in this country than there are route miles of all United States airlines combined.

Finally, when a great challenge, coupled with the possibility of great reward is presented, history indicates it attracts an adventurous breed. And when one challenge solved leads but to another, one may safely anticipate from such a group a remarkable display of resourcefulness. Such a generalization is not denied in the story of petroleum. Nor is a related generalization denied: that a new force, penetrating the established order with new methods and new ideas, generates friction, and if successful is due not only acclaim but envy.

Knowledge of petroleum and its seepage from the earth existed for more than eighteen and a half centuries before Christ, but it was not until eighteen and a half centuries after Christ that the petroleum industry was born of two great ideas. The first was to subject seeping oil to distillation. The second was not to depend upon seepages as a source of oil, but to drill directly into the underground "lake" from which the seeping oil was believed to come.

At least one man was purported to have argued with Colonel Drake that his idea was immoral; that the oil was needed down there for the fires of hell, and to withdraw it was to protect the wicked from the punishment which they so justly deserved. While this proved not to be the last criticism directed against the petroleum industry, it was at least among the most novel.

Drake found a small oil sand by the sheerest of accidents, as we know today. The second man to drill a well found no oil and thus it was early established that oil did not exist universally. Where does it exist? To answer that question the petroleum industry became the largest employer of men and women who were university trained in the earth sciences. Oil companies undertook research on which millions of dollars have been expended. It resulted not only in knowledge immediately useful to them; it also contributed in a major way to man's understanding of the earth on which he lives. The scientific instruments and methods used in the search for oil and gas are largely responsible for the hundred billion barrels of liquid petroleum so far discovered in the United States, and billions of barrels discovered in foreign countries.

Not all the discoveries have been based on a scientific approach, of course; the early oil man, and some who were not so early, relied upon hunch, dowsing, and even dreams and spiritualism. Even today there is no science that leads the explorer directly to oil, only to structures which may contain oil. To find out for sure, the oil man must put his money on the line for a well. Last year, eight out of nine wells drilled in unproven territory in the United States were failures, and even within proven areas, one out of four wells failed to find oil. One of the oil industry's most urgent challenges is to perfect more precise methods of oil exploration. Today's methods are producing fine results in foreign countries where the geography hasn't been picked over as thoroughly as it has in the United States. Here, however, we need a scientific breakthrough in finding the harder-to-find accumulations. It is a matter of intensive investigation.

One of Colonel Drake's problems in drilling his well was caused by subterranean water. It repeatedly caved in the hole. He was ingenious enough to drive a cast iron pipe into

31

hole and run his drill inside the pipe. Drake's well had be pumped from the start. The first flowing wells came into production in 1861. One of them produced 2,500 barrels a day for some eight months and then went out like a light. Another was choked off by paraffin. In 1865, a nitroglycerin charge was exploded at the bottom of a well and it resulted in an immediate, substantial increase in production. The inventor of the idea was on the road to riches. But one early driller who tried the method wound up with a dry hole, although the flow from his neighbor's well went up enormously! Such eccentricities gave the oil man an early introduction to several more of the special perversities of nature. Obviously, there was much to learn about oil reservoirs, how to reach them with a drill, how to produce them and how to treat them to prolong their lives.

A new specialization—petroleum engineering—developed to concentrate on problems of this kind. Through research, analysis and experimentation, although always dealing with unobservable phenomena as much as three or four miles underground, a vast body of knowledge has been developed. It is the foundation of present-day oil and gas conservation laws, of techniques for assisted and secondary recovery, and of the unitized operation of oil fields in which all interests are pooled and entire reservoirs are produced on sound engineering principles as though under single ownership.

New companies and whole new industries have been spawned by the demands of the oil explorers and producers. One of the most unusual, even though among the smallest, is the mud industry which does an annual volume of some 150 million dollars, supplying drilling fluids to the petroleum industry. Prime movers, the manufacturer of steel tubing, cement, explosives, all these and more have been affected by the insistence of the oil man on more effective and reliable tools and equipment to find and bring oil and gas from the earth. When the earth's mantle is penetrated in the interest of scientific investigation, as is proposed in the Mohole Project of the National Academy of Sciences, it will be the technology of the oil producer that puts the drill bit six or more miles below sea level.

The unique transportation problems created by the necessity of handling enormous quantities of bulk liquids and gases economically have already been mentioned. It is impossible to imagine the petroleum industry in present-day terms had oil men taken the attitude that transportation was no part of their business. Today the pipeline, which is to the petroleum industry as plumbing is to the house, has found at least a pioneering application in the transportation of powdered coal. The tankship is used for molasses and chemicals, and the tank truck for a number of products, including milk. The amazing increase in the last decade in consumption of natural gas, which as recently as 1947 represented less than 15 per cent of the country's energy requirement and today exceeds 30 per cent, is an outgrowth of the advancing technology of large-diameter pipelines for the transportation of liquid petroleum.

The art of making kerosine from crude oil might easily have been borrowed bodily from an older, somewhat more

33

heady application of the principle of distillation. One had only to substitute crude oil for mash, and presto! Seagram's Oil Company.

When it came to making lubricants, however, the oil refiner had to pioneer his own art. Whereas there had been an almost instantaneous market for kerosine as a superior, lower-cost substitute for available lamp oils, a decade or two passed before mineral lubricants began to win general acceptance. The newfangled lubricants made from rock oil were to be viewed suspiciously. With the coming of petroleum, however, lubrication became a science, and with the aid of science the refiner began to design lubricants for an infinite variety of specialized applications. He went on from there to produce oils whose function was less to lubricate than to serve some other special purpose; for example, dielectric oils to insulate high voltage transformers, and processing oils which make rubber more workable and extend its supply by entering into and becoming an inseparable part of the rubber itself.

Another fundamental discovery came early in the second decade of this century. By 1915, gasoline demand exceeded that for kerosine. Even before that time refiners bumped into the hard fact that nature had not put enough gasoline in crude oil to keep up with the soaring requirements of the automobile. In discovering how to break up oil fractions that were too heavy to burn in a gasoline engine, and thus increase gasoline yields, the way was found to effect a substantial increase in gasoline quality as well. In this beginning, the groundwork was laid for fuels for the high compression engine, in itself a great contribution to economy in air and automotive transportation. The process which helped solve the immediate gasoline supply problem was thermal cracking, patented in 1912. It was the first demonstration that the refiner could do more than separate his raw material; he could also transform it. The process was licensed for use by others at reasonable cost, setting a precedent highly significant in spreading advances in refining technology rapidly throughout the industry.

Oil refiners, spurred by the development of thermal cracking, launched research programs in earnest, eventually reaching a stage second only to the chemical industry itself in the employment of chemists. More highly sophisticated processes for altering the characteristics of hydrocarbons followed thermal cracking. Notable among them were processes employing catalysts to promote and control reactions.

By the time of World War II, the petroleum refiner had developed techniques capable of overcoming a dangerous undersupply of TNT, of creating a synthetic rubber industry almost overnight, and of providing superior aircraft performance for the Allied forces through the production of prodigious quantities of aviation fuels of 100 octane quality and better.

Yet, as striking as these accomplishments were, it is in the postwar period that the most amazing progress of petrochemistry has become evident. Today, the origin of some three thousand organic chemicals can be traced back to crude oil and natural gas, and in some instances the petroleum industry has become an important supplier of inorganic chemicals as well. Petrochemical production in the United States exceeds 42 billion pounds annually, equivalent to more than 50 per cent of the value of total United States output of chemicals.

In these recent years, many significant interreactions have resulted from the thrust of oil-refining technology. For example, the attack on the rubber shortage during World War II involved the production of huge quantities of pure butadiene. To attain the necessary degree of purity on a mass-production basis, refiners needed to know what was in the stream without waiting for chemical analysis. They went to the optical industry with ideas for infrared and ultraviolet sensing devices. A number of substantial businesses in the optical field grew out of the original needs and ideas of the petroleum refiners, and a direct outcome today are certain antimissile missiles whose infrared guidance systems seek out hot tail pipes aloft.

Petroleum refiners recognized forty years ago that their costs would go out of reach unless they operated large-capacity plants on a continuous-flow basis and in many respects automatically. From them came the impetus for instrumentation theory, and for a dozen years, beginning in the early twenties, practically all industrial instruments, aside from those to measure and control electricity, flowed into the petroleum industry. The birth of the industrial instruments industry is more to be attributed to the petroleum refiner than to any other industrial group.

With the development of catalytic cracking in the thirties, petroleum refiners needed instruments with built-in prescience—automatic controllers to handle programed sequences of large numbers of interrelated changes. Thus, they were in the forefront of automation, although they didn't know it, for the word had not yet been invented. The high degrees of automation being achieved in refining, as well as in production and pipeline operations, were simply matters of taking steps which came naturally to attain the result that had to be reached. The consequence of this resourcefulness in penetrating the unknown was low costs.

In marketing, it was primarily the demands of the automobile that challenged conventional concepts. Here was a new type of customer, on wheels, in a hurry, and the way to get his business was to make it easy for him to buy. The first service stations appeared as early as 1907, when automobile registrations totaled less than 105,000. From that point on, gasoline marketing has been shaped by the efforts of oil companies to respond to the whims of the motorist, to react to the realities of competition in thousands of separate geographical markets, and to adjust to the changing requirements of law—three forces, any one of which I might say could provide enough material for several speeches. Indeed, it seems difficult at times to comprehend that such a simple physical act as pumping gasoline into the fuel tanks of automobiles and collecting payment for it could set so much in motion, including, I might point out specifically, affectionate palpitations in the breasts of the nation's tax collectors.

Such time as is available in this particular presentation might be spent most usefully on two points. First, the petroleum industry, by adopting an engineering approach to cost-cutting, has achieved great economies in distribution. This is true, even though some 180,000 retail merchants, 14,000 wholesalers and about 200 refiners are involved in the gasoline marketing process. I believe I am correct in saying, that, pound for pound, no commodity is placed at the disposal of consumers at distribution costs which are as low as those the petroleum industry has been able to achieve. Yet, the attainment of still greater economies is diligently being sought within the industry, and that is a competitive pressure which no marketer can ignore.

The second point is that the marketing practices of the petroleum industry give full effect, at every crossroads, to a competitive drive that extends all the way back to the oil well. There is nothing passive about the marketing of gasoline. Competition is fostered dynamically and, except for wartime periods, the industry's history has been marked by a constant condition of plentiful supply stemming from the pressures I sought to describe earlier.

The same pressures—to produce, to sell—were primary motivations in the emergence of vertical integration within the petroleum industry. Additional pressures came from the fact that the unique, single-purpose facilities required for the economical processing and handling of petroleum involve substantial capital investments at levels of risk which would be prohibitive in the absence of some assurance of near-capacity rates of use. As demands upon the industry grew, it became essential, if continuity of supply were to be maintained and economic waste avoided, that the successive functions be integrated under a single corporate management, or that the same result be sought through integration by contract. As an economist might state it, there is great disutility, for example, in a pipeline which has no source of supply or no outlet.

Integration in the petroleum industry has often been attacked as a nefarious scheme hatched for evil purposes. It is demonstrable, however, that integration first appeared, not as a means to monopoly, but rather as a weapon against monopoly. An eminently desirable test of goodness or evil in a society dedicated to the supremacy of the individual, is performance in the interest of the consuming public. Judged by that criterion, vertical integration in the petroleum industry passes with flying colors.

Among other things, integration facilitated the accumulation of capital resources committed to the great undertakings that have been necessary in maintaining adequate supplies. Even so, the largest of integrated companies have been too small to undertake alone the risks involved in many oil industry operations. Underwater drilling, deep exploratory tests in virgin territory, constructing large-diameter long distance pipelines, and the development of foreign oil are examples.

As a consequence, many forms of risk-sharing have been developed and are common in the financial management of oil companies. Risk-sharing may range from a simple agreement to pay part of the cost of drilling a well, provided it proves to be a dry hole, to a full partnership in all costs and gains in exploring for oil in a foreign country.

Risk-sharing reflects the generally conservative financial practices through which the petroleum industry seeks to moderate as best it can the hazards of its occupation. It plows back a larger share of profits than does manufacturing industry generally. It seeks to charge current operations with current costs to the greatest possible degree. It was, for example, among the first to adopt the last-in, first-out method of inventory valuation, which has the effect of offsetting, at least to some extent, the erosion of inflation.

Integration's greatest value, as previously indicated, is its effect, all along the chain of operations, of focusing concern on the ultimate consumer. How well has the petroleum industry served the consumer? Gasoline is a fair—even a severe —test of this question for the reason that since the early years it has faced no competition from alternative fuels. It has had a practical monopoly in the propulsion of automobiles. Yet, consider this brief comparison. In 1919, the year in which the first excise tax was placed on gasoline, it sold at the service station at an annual average price of 25½ cents per gallon. For the first nine months of 1959, the average amount the motorist paid was 30 cents, but 9 cents of the total represented local, state, and federal gasoline taxes. The price, excluding taxes, was down one-sixth while the cost of living was up two-thirds. Moreover, the quality of 1959 regular-grade gasoline, as measured by the rise in octane number alone, is at least 60 per cent better than the 1919 product.

It seems clear to me, in considering comparisons of this kind, that the petroleum industry has taken much of the shock out of gasoline taxes as far as the motorist is concerned. Through its accomplishments in reducing unit costs, it is in effect offsetting the bill for a large part of the increasing tax burden levied on gasoline consumers. No one can say what the level of gasoline consumption might be under more moderate taxes. Nor can anyone say how successful the industry will be in continuing to insulate consumers from the tax load which, as all of you know, increased a further one cent on October 1. When the tax on an essential commodity reaches the point that it virtually equals the manufacturer's price, as gasoline taxes do today, one may wonder whether the government purse is being fattened at the expense of the long-range public interest.

In serving the public through low prices, the petroleum industry has not done so at the expense of its employees. On the contrary, they are among the highest paid in the country and they enjoy fringe benefits which are unequaled. The industry's efficiency is primarily the result of heavy capital investment. Its gross investment was nearly 63 billion dollars at the end of last year, making it the nation's third largest industry. Capital expenditures at the rate of five to six billion dollars a year are common to the industry. Its profits on investments are about average for industry generally. This is a confounding fact to those who seem bent on convincing the public that the petroleum industry is a profiteer waxing fat on tax windfalls provided by percentage depletion.

In discussing the petroleum revolution within the allotted time, I have found it necessary to omit whole subject areas, and in other cases to limit or exclude validating evidence for what may seem flat assertions. But basic to all that I have said is the thesis, first, that petroleum presented great challenges in science, technology, organization, finance, and persuasion. Secondly, these challenges were accepted because the incentive and freedom to do so existed. Thirdly, the resourcefulness with which the challenges were met had a multiplying effect in contributing to the well-being of mankind. Finally, the performance of the petroleum industry is a testament to the efficacy of a system of maximum individual liberty and minimum governmental license in promoting economic progress.

To me, the future appears to hold great opportunities for the oil man. Seldom has he been under such pressure as he is today to achieve new breakthroughs which will improve the profitability of his business. Never has he spent more in researching his problems than he is spending now—a total estimated at 300 million dollars annually. If history is a guide, thinking in terms of the long span of history as was so ably set forth by Professor Nevins, nothing but good will come from this.

However, I shall listen with the keenest attention this afternoon to Dr. Teller, Dr. Mason, and the Honorable Herbert Hoover, Jr., for there are aspects of the future which are clouded by the penetration of noneconomic forces into the functioning of an industry which has always performed best in an atmosphere of economic freedom.

The course of the second hundred years of the petroleum revolution depends, I believe, upon the extent to which the atmosphere of economic freedom is preserved in America.

Thank you.

DEAN BROWN: Mr. Dunlop, in thirty-five minutes you have sketched the history of a hundred years of extraordinary growth, development and achievement.

The thing that interested me most was your delineation of the several markets the petroleum business has had. Starting with the lighting business, then developing vigorously in the transportation business, to a point where, at one time, I dare say, the industry thought of gasoline as the only prime product and everything else almost in terms of by-products, you have in more recent decades been getting into the heating business, and even more recently, into the petrochemical business, where you may be moving away from energy entirely. Do you see the great future development of the industry in any one of these four fields, more than others?

MR. DUNLOP: Well, not being a crystal-ball gazer, it is rather difficult to be too definite in answering your question. I would like to say this. In indicating that the industry has gone from one field to another, you have emphasized the fact that it has been an extremely versatile industry and one which has been characterized by a high degree of re-

43

sourcefulness. As competitive pressures have been brought into play, the industry has exercised its resourcefulness and moved along into the future in terms of the development of new opportunities.

You mentioned chemicals. I believe development in that direction is going to continue. I have great respect for the versatility of the industry. The future is going to be determined by the extent to which these qualities and characteristics can continue to find free play amongst those who are members of the industry.

It is true that competitive fuels will come in to an increasing extent. I suspect that certain of the markets which we have heretofore enjoyed will no longer be available to us, because low-cost energy in other forms will come into being.

I do think that we have a tremendous horizon before us in the petrochemical field. I'm still of the opinion that we are going to have the internal combustion engine—for good or ill, if you tried to get across some of these streets this morning as I did, not knowing exactly where I was going, you know what I mean. I'm sure the gasoline engine is going to be here for a while.

So some of our more settled opportunities are still with us and there will be others that will come up as the opportunities arise.

DEAN BROWN: Thank you. Here is a question that will give you the opportunity perhaps to brag about the industry just a little bit. What has the oil industry done for its own employees, while performing the great accomplishments for the public?

MR. DUNLOP: That seems almost like a loaded question, doesn't it? As I mentioned very briefly without giving any validating support, the oil industry has done a great deal for its employees. Oil industry workers are among the highest paid in the United States; on occasion they are the highest paid. Sometimes they jockey back and forth a bit with those engaged in coal, and those engaged in the chemical industry itself. One of the great virtues, however, in being an oil employee is the fact that you enjoy relatively continuous employment, so that when you take our hourly rates, which are very high, and project them on a weekly or monthly basis, they present a striking figure.

As far as fringe benefits are concerned, the industry today is spending somewhere between 20 and 25 cents on the direct labor dollar for fringe benefits, which compares extremely favorably with other sorts of economic endeavor in the United States.

DEAN BROWN: The next question is a bit on the philosophical side, dealing with science. You point to necessity as the mother of inventions, for which other uses are then found. Mr. Nevins pleads for pure science, a dedicated search for truth. Which approach do you believe the most potent?

MR. DUNLOP: I would like to share Professor Nevins' point of view when he answered a similar question a little earlier. He indicated that a balance between various phases of endeavor is very necessary, and certainly I share his

45

thought that the basic, fundamental scientific effort being undertaken in the universities and similar centers is important, extremely important. And we, in the oil industry, in applying the developments that come out of basic research, from those fine minds, are their beneficiaries. We are given the opportunity to put to work the principles which they develop.

I don't think there can be progress in the United States or in any of the other free countries of the world without there being a proper balance of effort in both those areas. You could take any one of the developments that I made reference to and you would find that much of the basic work had been done in fine universities or institutions of similar character, before they were brought into the petroleum industry and utilized.

DEAN BROWN: This is a question that I am sure we are going to reach in this afternoon's discussion, but since you are now on your feet and are the one representative of the oil business on this program, it may be appropriate to ask it of you now. The increasing difficulty of finding oil suggests a diminishing national supply. Is it time, therefore, to think of changing our import laws which encourage use of domestic supplies as against cheaper foreign reserves?

MR. DUNLOP: You have indicated that that subject will be dealt with later much more adequately than I can deal with it now. You know, I looked forward to coming here today. I thought to myself, in preparing this presentation, "For once in your life, Dunlop, you come as a noncontroversial figure. You will be in an academic atmosphere, and you are going to speak as the only representative of the petroleum industry; therefore, you don't have to worry about controversial points of view."

I'm sure that the person who asked this question had in mind the present problems that exist and are seeking solution in the import program that is being administered so ably by Captain Carson, whom I am delighted to see here in the audience.

I don't think you can look at that problem by itself. I think you've got to look at the broader spectrum of problems in that field. We think in terms of imports as having created so many of our difficulties, and exclude natural gas. As I pointed out, natural gas now supplies some 30 per cent of the energy requirements of this country, while immediately after the war it supplied just half that figure. This is a great thrust of competitive influence which is competing with its companion hydrocarbons for the consumer market.

It is true we have had a great increase in discoveries abroad, and most of those discoveries result in the production of oil at lower costs than can be achieved here in the United States.

I think a genuine effort is being made to bring these various problems into balance. I'm one of the persuasion that the great need of this country is to continue to have an aggressive, virile, domestic industry, and I do think that it is necessary that steps be taken to preserve it. I think that very substantial headway has been made in that regard.

47

DEAN BROWN: I have just two more questions and then I think we will terminate the morning session. Mr. Dunlop, would you care to comment on future technological trends in your industry?

MR. DUNLOP: I presume this means future methods of finding oil, future methods of refining oil, and perhaps using oil. A tremendous effort is being put forth. I mentioned the sum of about 300 million dollars that is being expended annually in research. It is being expended on a fairly balanced basis, as you know. We are not finding oil as well as we believe we should find it here in the United States, and there is a great deal of effort going into the development of new principles, new techniques, which we hope will result in increased oil discovery here.

You are all familiar with the tremendous advancements that have been made technologically in transportation. They are a little more clearly recognizable because you can see the results. I think those activities will continue. Several weeks ago we, ourselves, launched a ship, the third ship bearing the same name. The first ship, which was built some thirty-five years ago, had an annual capacity of some two million barrels on the Gulf Coast to north of Hatteras run. The one that has just been delivered will have an annual capacity of some ten million barrels, a fivefold increase. The new ship's crew is only between 10 to 15 per cent larger than the first ship's—very clear-cut evidence of what technology is able to do in the way of increasing the productive capacity of people.

I'm sure there is a great deal of work being done in refineries. I know, in my own company and in those companies with which I have an association, that petrochemicals show a real promise, particularly just now. There is tremendous research effort being made in seeking, not only better ways to produce gasoline and to make an improved product, but to open up new areas of opportunity. I suppose that the greatest effort is being made in that area and that it will continue.

Being of a balanced persuasion, I wouldn't neglect the marketing department and I'm sure that there are many people here today—I see them in this audience—who are very conscious of the great effort that is being made to merchandise our products so that we can even surpass our own past record.

Summing it up, I suspect that the great emphasis, in terms of total dollars, is in the field of the development of new products which we hope to make available to the American public.

DEAN BROWN: The last question of this morning's session is a question that you may wish to, in turn, question with respect to its assumptions, but nevertheless, because it has been submitted, I want to ask it.

Since management of private business first plans where it is going before undertaking a business project, isn't such an approach appropriate in charting the energy future of this country, and why does the oil business oppose a positive energy policy and support an accidental one?

MR. DUNLOP: I agree with you. I think I do need a little more information. I would question that the oil industry opposes an aggressive program of energy development. But as to the problems with which the oil industry is confronted, we have several points of view that we have to consider. We have to consider the long-range point of view as well as the short-range point of view in conducting our affairs on a day-to-day basis. And I believe the oil industry, in considering the long-range energy requirements of this country and of the free peoples of the world, thinks objectively and on a balanced basis.

Sometimes the short run and the long run may come into conflict, but I think, from the experience I have had and the knowledge of my own relationships, we are in sympathy with the continued development of low-cost sources of energy for the American people, and we would be hopeful that we, in the oil industry, would be sufficiently alert to our opportunities in that regard that through science, through research and development, we will continue to be one of the very substantial suppliers of that energy.

DEAN BROWN: The Chairmanship of the morning session being my excuse for doing so, I am going to interject just one more question that relates to this. It puts the question on a broader canvas.

We are all interested, I am sure, in the development not only of this country, but of the rest of the world. Is there sufficient attention and thoughtfulness being given, in your view, Mr. Dunlop, to the development of energy as a balanced part of the development of other parts of the world, particularly the less developed parts? Are we doing enough in the way of developing the energy components in our efforts to make it easier for other peoples to help themselves?

Mr. Dunlop: That's very difficult to answer because it is a question of degree.

Obviously there is always more to be done. I think a tremendous effort is going forth and I'm—well, my reaction is that the effort is going forth in a large degree through what we would term, in this country, free principles, and for that reason it may not seem to be as well co-ordinated or as highly developed as possibly it should be.

Being of the persuasion that I am, I think that the effort should continue along those lines. There may be an opportunity for a higher degree of co-ordination of that effort. But I would just like to say one thing. I would like to pick up what Professor Nevins said so ably. The whole development of energy in its relationship to the culture of Western man has been essentially a matter of the spirit. As a representative of the oil industry, it is my conviction that the worthwhile things this industry has accomplished over its hundred years of history, have been primarily those things on which the spirit of man has had a free opportunity to be exercised.

And so, I would like to close with this thought. The oil industry very definitely shares Dr. Nevins' concept that the future well-being of people is related not to material advantages, but rather to the freedom of the spirit and that the material advantages will flow from that.

III. ENERGY PATTERNS OF THE FUTURE

by Edward Teller

LADIES AND GENTLEMEN, I AM TO TALK TO YOU ABOUT ENERGY in the future. I will start by telling you why I believe that the energy resources of the past must be supplemented. First of all, these energy resources will run short as we use more and more of the fossil fuels.

We find that more and more such fuel is being discovered and I am quite sure that within the present century there need not be an acute shortage of any of the fuels to which we are accustomed. But the demand for fuel is rising—and rising substantially—and new fuel deposits are usually discovered in locations which are a little less accessible than those which we have already used, and so the price of the fuel will go up.

In fact, this process, as you all know, has already started. The price of fuel has been creeping up steadily, and the price of energy has been kept relatively low and steady, only because while the price of fuel is rising, the utilization of the fuel has been increasing.

In our modern energy-producing machinery, we utilize approximately one-third of the energy of the fuel and while there are possibilities of increasing this utilization to one-half or two-thirds, we certainly won't utilize it 100 per cent, and even the further increase which is now in prospect begins to come a little hard. Therefore, it begins to be of real interest to see what else we can do and what we can use for fuel.

Furthermore, fuel, in some places of the world, is cheap. In other places, where there are no close-by coal or, particularly, oil deposits, fuel is much more expensive, and therefore large regions of our globe are, at least to some extent, retarded on account of absence of usable fuel.

There are all kinds of alternative possibilities which have been considered, and which I will discuss later. But I would first like to mention another reason why we probably have to look for additional fuel supplies. And this, strangely, is the question of contaminating the atmosphere. Now, all of us are familiar with smoke and smog and all of us know about it as a nuisance. Perhaps it is also a hazard, but certainly it is a nuisance, with which we are all familiar.

I would like to talk to you about a more hypothetical difficulty which I think is quite probably going to turn out to be real. Whenever you burn conventional fuel, you create carbon dioxide. It has been calculated that the carbon dioxide which has been put into the atmosphere since the beginning of the industrial revolution equals approximately 10 per cent of the amount of carbon dioxide that our atmosphere contained originally.

There are modern methods by which we can find out reasonably accurately how much of this additional carbon dioxide the atmosphere actually contains today. They are the result of some excellent work at the Scripps Institute in California, and through these methods it was found that actually the carbon dioxide content of the atmosphere has increased by only 2 per cent.

It will interest you, perhaps, to hear how this was found out, and I can tell you in a very short time. A certain fraction of the carbon that is in the carbon dioxide is very weakly radioactive, and this activity can be traced back to the effect of cosmic rays which produce carbon in the atmosphere. The carbon dioxide which is now in the atmosphere is a little bit less radioactive than the carbon dioxide that was in the atmosphere thirty, forty, fifty, one hundred years ago. You can still sample that old carbon dioxide by investigating wood that grew thirty or forty or one hundred years ago, and this slightly aged wood is more active. What has happened? In the intervening years we have burned a lot of the material which had been deposited in the carboniferous era and at other times, times so long ago that in the meantime the carbon in the coal or the carbon in the petroleum has lost its radioactivity. So part of the carbon in our atmosphere is not radioactive carbon, but ancient inactive carbon.

Ten per cent has been added, 2 per cent is found present. The rest is in the ocean, mostly on the bottom of the ocean, precipitated as calcium carbonate. We now know that most of the carbon has gone this way, and that the atmosphere contains only that much additional carbon as has

57

been burned in the last ten or fifteen years. That is the residence time of the carbon dioxide in the atmosphere.

If now, the rate of burning conventional fuels continues to increase by a factor of 2 each ten years, the result will be that by the end of the century there will be an increase of carbon dioxide in the atmosphere by more than 10 per cent. The carbon dioxide is invisible, it is transparent, you can't smell it, it is not dangerous to health, so why should one worry about it?

Carbon dioxide has a strange property. It transmits visible light but it absorbs the infrared radiation which is emitted from the earth. Its presence in the atmosphere causes a greenhouse effect in that it will allow the solar rays to enter, but it will to some extent impede the radiation from the earth into outer space.

The result is that the earth will continue to heat up until a balance is re-established. Then the earth will be at a higher temperature and will radiate more. It has been calculated that a temperature rise corresponding to a 10 per cent increase in carbon dioxide will be sufficient to melt the icecap and submerge New York. All the coastal cities would be covered, and since a considerable percentage of the human race lives in coastal regions, I think that this chemical contamination is more serious than most people tend to believe.

For this then, and for many other reasons, I will say that any new fuels we find will be welcome. I believe that of the new fuels, nuclear energy is the most promising and I will talk about nuclear energy from here on.

Nuclear fuel has, of course, been saved—its energy content has not been released, because atomic nuclei repel each other so violently that except under extraordinary circumstances they cannot come into contact. And only when they come into contact do they release the energies which reside in them, energies that are a million times greater than chemical energy.

In the last couple of decades, we have learned how to release these nuclear energies. All of you are familiar with nuclear fission, how a uranium atom may split into two parts, releasing a lot of energy and some neutrons, how these neutrons can approach further nuclei, how this process then can repeat and multiply, creating what is known as a chain reaction and giving rise to fabulous amounts of energy connected with small amounts of material.

In the early years of the Second World War we learned how to tame this energy, how to build nuclear reactors which would release such energy. The first nuclear reactor went into operation a little less than eighteen years ago. Nuclear reactors are still not economically competitive. Why not? What is holding us up?

There are two answers that I could give, a wrong answer and a right answer. I will give you the wrong answer first. The wrong answer is that we first must solve the question of raw materials. Uranium, as we dig it out of the ground, is usable for reactors only in a somewhat clumsy manner. One has to do one of two things, either to separate isotopes, or to achieve what is known as breeding. All these problems are extremely interesting and I will spend a very few minutes to discuss them with you.

Uranium contains 99.3 per cent of a sluggish, relatively less useful isotope and .7 per cent of a red-hot isotope, Uranium 235. The straightforward method is to separate these isotopes and use the active part. Once you have that active part, it is easy to make a good reactor. We used to believe that the separation was too expensive. Many people still believe it. We are producing today this isotope at an announced price, and if you compare this cost with that of gasoline or coal, BTU for BTU and dollar for dollar, you find that the modern nuclear fuels already prepared and separated cost only 70 per cent of what you pay for a conventional fuel.

Therefore, the price of the nuclear fuel is not an excuse. This is the wrong answer. Still, I will pursue this question of price because there is a further possible development in store and a very interesting one, too. While a nuclear reactor works, it not only produces energy, it also can produce some additional nuclear species, in particular, Plutonium, and this process is known as breeding.

One uses up the active material, but at the same time, one activates inactive material. The result is that when this process is fully worked out (and it is not worked out yet) you can expect a great additional drop in the fuel price.

This breeding or activation, which I have described to you, won't work unless you have some fertile material available, and there are only two fertile materials—Uranium and Thorium. What about their supply?

They are cheap today, but won't they run short? Well, they won't for a hundred years. And furthermore, they won't for millions of years, if we find reasonably cheap methods to separate Uranium and Thorium from materials in which these substances are contained only in small percentages. We are making progress in using ores in which only one-tenth of a per cent is Uranium or Thorium and I think in the course of time, we may find methods by which we can extract the few parts per million of Uranium that are contained in very common substances, like granite.

You should realize that once this procedure is worked out, we can extract from a ton of granite, in the end, more heat than from a ton of coal. But first you must separate out the Uranium and then you must do something with this Uranium to use all of it, to breed it. If you can accomplish all of this—and it won't be easy—then we will literally be able to burn rocks, and the fuel problem will have been solved once and for all.

Now, in view of this, in view of this great future and in view of the present cheap price of Uranium 235, why aren't the light bulbs in this hall actuated by nuclear reactors, which they are not, to the best of my information? The reason is that in the course of fission, radioactivities are produced, the reactor is hot, dangerous to approach, and must be handled by distant control equipment.

All this is not only expensive in itself, it also slows down research directed toward better methods, cheaper methods, of producing energy. Even today in conventional fuels, half

61

the expense of producing energy is in capital equipment and operation, and only half of it in raw materials.

Operation and capital investment is much greater in the case of nuclear fuel, and the main question is how to find ways and means to improve nuclear technology so that operation and capital investment will drop. I am quite sure that this can be accomplished, although in order to accomplish it, we will need many talented nuclear engineers and so far there is no overabundance.

I would like to pursue an associated thought for a moment. What about this dangerous material which makes it so difficult to approach a nuclear reactor? What kind of consequences does it have otherwise? Are nuclear reactors dangerous? Well, I dare say yes, it is dangerous if a nuclear reactor malfunctions. It can release the radioactive poisons contained in it and it can contaminate many, many square miles in the down-wind direction.

Now, at this point, I should like to draw a sharp distinction between this kind of contamination and the so-called fallout about which there has been so much popular agitation. The fallout coming from tests is so negligible that it is certainly and demonstrably smaller than that from a great number of natural effects to which we don't give any thought. The danger of fallout from nuclear activity has been exaggerated to such an extent that I feel that the only real medical hazard has become the hazard of stomach ulcers.

I should particularly point out that a very serious scientific question exists on whether these exceedingly low-level activities coming from world-wide fallout have or have not any harmful effect. Nobody knows, but it is clearly demonstrated that they have no more harmful effects, in fact, less harmful effects, than the effect from cosmic rays on those who live at some elevated position, say, Denver, Colorado. At the same time, concentrated fallout is bad. What a nuclear reactor can do if it malfunctions and spreads its radioactivity over the countryside is most serious. This should be guarded against extremely carefully, and indeed very great precautions have been taken to avoid nuclear accidents. With good luck and very conscientious work, the Atomic Energy Commission and everybody else connected with the undertaking have so far avoided such accidents.

It is essential that we maintain this good record, and we must find methods at the same time to lower the price of all procedures connected with nuclear energy. This is a big and important and detailed and nasty engineering job, but one which I am sure will be solved in the course of time.

One last word about reactors. Since it is such a big and difficult job, it is extremely important to concentrate on the most hopeful and most easy aspects of it. I am much more interested in stationary nuclear reactors than in any nuclear reactor which moves. I am talking about civilian application. Wherever there is motion, there is greater hazard.

To be quite specific, I think that we are going to need our gasoline for many decades, perhaps for centuries, in order to drive our cars, or fly our planes. I think the neat, handy, chemical energy package of gasoline is something which we shall not be able to replace for a long time.

Therefore, I advocate that we replace our stationary energy generators as soon as it is economic by the more abundant nuclear power, and save our petroleum for mobile equipment and for petrochemicals. I think that is a reasonable, long-range view.

But it is not necessarily the end of our mission. There are other things in the offing. In 1951 and 1952, when thermonuclear power produced the first hydrogen bomb, we were asked: "It is clear that fusion can be used in war. What about using fusion in peace? It is the same reaction, isn't it?"

Well, it is the same reaction, but that's not what counts. It is easy to blow up something; it is much more difficult to make it react at a slow and controllable rate. Greek fire saved Constantinople from the Moslems more than a thousand years ago, and a millennium had to elapse before this chemical energy became usable in a controlled fashion. Well, we are not going to take a thousand years to control nuclear energy. But we are going to take some time, and I will tell you why.

In order to make thermonuclear fuel work slowly we must use the material in great dilution. We use as few atoms, or rather positive and negative ions, as would correspond ordinarily to a high vacuum. But it is a high pressure vacuum because of the high temperature, so that few particles produce many atmospheres.

Under these conditions, the reaction would be comfortable and slow, but these hot particles will bump into the wall and lose their energy. What to do about that?

We have to invent a medium which contains the ions without depriving them of their heat content, and that can be done. There is such a medium—magnetism, magnetic lines of force which induce the ionized particles to spiral around them and which keep the particles away from cool walls.

In principle, all of this is very simple. It is the same kind of problem as to try and confine a high pressure gas in a bottle made out of rubber bands. The magnetic lines of force have certain properties similar to rubber bands. They can be pushed aside and the hot gas can leak out in between. Then we lose it and lose its energy.

Well, we found that indeed—excuse me for the horrible word—this magneto-hydro-dynamic-instability does actually take place. Nor is it the only kind of instability that occurs. This gas, which consists of positive and negative ions, insists when you try to work with it, on starting to oscillate. The positive and negative ions beat against each other and the oscillation, in turn, induces phenomena like turbulence, which give rise to a loss of the valuable gas.

The situation is a little bit similar to that in the art of flying a hundred years ago. Then, people were worried about turbulence in aerodynamics and there were gentlemen who proved that to fly is impossible. We had at least one encouragement in those days, those of us who were around: we could see the birds fly. Today, we have only one kind of model for natural thermonuclear energy release, and that is the model furnished by the sun and the stars. This model we cannot copy so easily because the sun and the stars do it by the brute force method, or perhaps what is even worse, by sheer inertia.

We have to do it more cleverly. If we do it, we will have a cleaner fuel, we will have an abundant fuel, and by having worked out the appropriate method of confinement by magnetic lines of force, we shall automatically be able to generate electricity without moving parts, without moving anything, except the magnetic lines of force.

Can we do it? Almost ten years ago, I was asked the same question about hydrogen bombs, and I couldn't do anything but enumerate some doubts and difficulties, such as those I am putting before you now. And when one in the audience said, "Well, Edward, we saw such difficulties four years ago. Do you know whether you can do the thing now?" I said, "No." When they asked, "So what is the progress as compared to what you told us in 1945?" I was forced to say, "Today we don't know the answer on the basis of much better evidence."

We have done a lot in the last seven years in exploring the properties, all the possible instabilities, of exceedingly hot ionized gases. We begin to understand them. We begin to know how to avoid them. Perhaps we may even get an inkling of how to use them.

Today, we don't know the answer on the basis of much better evidence, and I believe it is extremely important that work on controlled fusion continue because the end result is valuable and its eventual achievement is probable. Maybe it will be the year 2000, maybe it will be even later. In the meantime, we will have learned a lot about electric discharges, about how to use a hot gas in a bottle, and there are all kinds of amusing uses of that.

I still have one other, more fantastic and, I believe, more feasible project to cover. And this is Project Plowshare, the peaceful use, not merely of nuclear energy, but of nuclear explosions.

A nuclear explosion is cheap and big, and it can be used for earth-moving jobs. You could dig harbors, you could dig water-level canals. You can break up rock formation, impermeable rock formation underground, and you could regulate water seepage and water flow below the surface. You can use it in mining. You can use it in a strange way in energy production, because you might make a big explosion very deep down in the ground and then mine the heat as today volcanic heat is mined in both Italy and New Zealand, converted into live steam and used to turn turbines.

All this can be done in principle. The easiest of these undertakings, the digging of canals and harbors, what I would like to call geographical engineering, is not only feasible, it is demonstrably possible.

We, furthermore, can undertake a beautiful exercise. I like to call it the exercise of putting the cart before the horse: using nuclear energy to get more oil.

How do we do it? With the help of nuclear explosives, you can blow up several hundred feet of overburden from a shale deposit, and you may strip-mine these shales.

There are other methods. We know, at least to some extent, how to break up underground formations. We might make the material more porous, pump out the oil more easily, and furthermore, open up for exploitation gooey or solid substances like tar sands or shales. If once they are broken up, they might be accessible to a heat-carrying fluid which will allow a release of more of the oil.

All these are dreams, but dreams which to some extent will come true, if only we are permitted to experiment with the effect of nuclear explosions. Furthermore, there is one great surprise in store for us if the development is not stopped. We are on the track of making completely clean nuclear explosions, explosions which will leave no radioactive fallout, which will not have any of the dangers of reactors and not even the slight dangers of the present world-wide fallout associated with them. If we have that, our blasting of canals and harbors, and carrying out of other plans, can proceed with great ease and great safety and great flexibility.

If people will not be too nervous, if progress is not stopped, this can be done. I would like to close on this one idea. When I read the novels of Jules Verne (and I'm sorry I haven't read them for a few years, because my children have outgrown them) I am struck by one thing more than by anything else: I'm struck by his optimistic attitude. When a new big possibility comes up fraught with uncertainty and with danger, he says: "Let's try it." In contrast, today's science fiction doesn't tell us anything, except how terrible, how dreadful the consequences of science will be.

The Russians in the last two or three years have performed eight explosions at or above one kiloton. They have announced their intention of blasting at the level of thirty kilotons. They have claimed, and we have not checked, that these explosions have not been nuclear. I think that the future will belong to those people who will look ahead in a positive and constructive way and who, after taking all the many and necessary safety precautions, will proceed confidently toward imaginative goals.

Thank you very much.

DEAN BROWN: We have taken a rather spectacular journey since ten o'clock this morning. We started with man, developing energy in the form of wind power and water power, and we have just been shown a vista of man's developing electric power without moving parts, as a result of our study of thermal gases.

I know that there are many questions that you will have of Dr. Teller. I would like to ask one question to start. It's a clarifying question, Dr. Teller. As I understood your comments, nuclear fuel, as fuel, BTU for BTU, is perhaps about 70 per cent as costly today as conventional fuel. The adaptation of nuclear fuel to useful purposes, however, involves a high security hazard, and it is this latter, as I understood your comments, that puts the additional costs on the end product of fuel produced from nuclear sources. Is that correct?

DR. TELLER: Yes, but I would also put a slightly different interpretation on it. The cost comes from the capital equipment and the handling. If, today, by magic, all the radio-

69

active hazards would vanish, these costs of capital equipment and handling still would remain great, but because of greater flexibility, both in research and in actual application, they would start dropping, in my opinion, very fast.

Capital equipment and handling costs have remained high because radioactivity imposes all kinds of limitations, both on the actual execution of the job and on the research connected with the job.

DEAN BROWN: Here is another clarifying question. Would you please summarize briefly the danger from increased carbon dioxide content in the atmosphere in this century?

DR. TELLER: At present the carbon dioxide in the atmosphere has risen by 2 per cent over normal. By 1970, it will be perhaps 4 per cent, by 1980, 8 per cent, by 1990, 16 per cent, if we keep on with our exponential rise in the use of purely conventional fuels. By that time, there will be a serious additional impediment for the radiation leaving the earth. Our planet will get a little warmer. It is hard to say whether it will be 2 degrees Fahrenheit or only one or 5.

But when the temperature does rise by a few degrees over the whole globe, there is a possibility that the icecaps will start melting and the level of the oceans will begin to rise. Well, I don't know whether they will cover the Empire State Building or not, but anyone can calculate it by looking at the map and noting that the icecaps over Greenland and over Antarctica are perhaps five thousand feet thick.

DEAN BROWN: I am going to ask Dr. Teller two more questions before we turn to the next speaker. If a truly clean bomb is just over the horizon, can this clean process be harnessed on a controlled basis, thus eliminating the need for elaborate safety precautions in stationary nuclear power plants?

DR. TELLER: The clean process is based on the thermonuclear process. Fusion reactions can be carried out cleanly. But as I have tried to explain to you, the fusion reaction has its own difficulties. Fission produces unavoidably a great variety of radioactive substances and some of these are really disagreeable.

Therefore, the fission process cannot be cleaned up.

DEAN BROWN: You have dealt, Dr. Teller, with combustion and nuclear energy. How do you view the future of fuel cells and other means of energy conversion currently being investigated?

DR. TELLER: The fuel cells, are, of course, a really wonderful idea and there have been signs recently that fuel cells will be highly successful. I would say that discussion of the fuel cells belongs primarily with the ways that the fuels are exploited, rather than in a discussion of the fuels themselves. Fuel cells will perhaps make it possible to use conventional fuel with better efficiency and also to use it much more conveniently.

Fuel cells could be run on solar energy and this, in turn, might be most useful for certain purposes like heating of isolated houses or like objects even farther away, such as satellites. Such conversion of solar energy directly into electricity would be a most wonderful invention. I believe that the direct conversion of heat into electricity is something that should be given the most serious consideration in con-

71

nection with nuclear reactors, too, because a nuclear reactor today works in the rather clumsy fashion of first giving the energy to a heat transfer liquid, creating problems of heat transfer, corrosion and everything else, and then letting this liquid, in turn, do the work outside the reactor.

There is a possibility that a future reactor will spew out electricity without any intermediate agency and under those conditions the cooling of the reactor could occur at much lower temperatures, with much less difficulty and with much less corrosion.

Therefore, this whole development of direct conversion into electricity is a very fertile and interesting field. I have not referred to it in my talk because it has not much to do with my topic but I am grateful to be given the opportunity to comment on it.

Thank you very much.

IV. LOW-COST AND ABUNDANT ENERGY

by Edward S. Mason

DR. MASON: MR. CHAIRMAN, LADIES AND GENTLEMEN: IT is clear that the subjects that have been assigned to me and to the next speaker overlap to some as yet undisclosed extent. Mr. Hoover and I tried to do our best to limit this overlap in correspondence, but it proves extraordinarily difficult to slice up this subject.

One way of dividing it might be to let me talk about economics, let him talk about politics and government, but in the energy field, economics and politics seem to be very difficult to divide.

Another way of slicing up the field might be to let me talk about the domestic problems, let him talk about the international problems, but again, in the international field, it is awfully difficult to separate the problem that way.

So, although I am going to do my best to stick to economic issues, I don't think I'm going to be able to limit myself to these issues. The fact of the matter is that this is not a problem that ought to be assigned to a pure economist, but then, on the other hand, I'm not a pure economist anyway, so I don't mind taking it.

Two basic natural resources problems have increasingly demanded public attention during the last few decades. How can we feed a rapidly growing world population from a relatively limited supply of arable land? And how can we meet rapidly increasing energy requirements at real costs that—if they do not decline—at least will not increase very much? It is the energy problem that concerns us today and, in a sense, it is the prior question. If the supply of arable land is to be increased by conventional irrigation methods energy requirements are large. And a really great expansion of arable land awaits the introduction of practical methods of desalting sea water with accompanying energy requirements that are enormous. Thus the answer to the question, "How are we going to feed rapidly increasing populations?" depends significantly on the availability of low-cost and abundant energy.

But agricultural output is not the only natural resource claimant on energy supplies. As we dig deeper into the earth's surface for minerals and metals and follow veins that become thinner or unearth deposits of poorer and poorer quality the energy input per unit of output inevitably rises. A meeting of increasing requirements for mineral raw materials without sharply rising costs is in large part an energy problem. If we could be assured of really low-cost and abundant energy, our concern about dwindling mineral supplies would be substantially reduced. They are all available in the earth's crust and in the seas in what are—for our purposes—unlimited quantities, and the cost of extraction is to a considerable extent an energy cost. In an important sense, therefore, it may be said that *the* natural resource problem is essentially a problem of low-cost and abundant energy.

The way these problems are handled, however, will seriously affect mankind only a half-century or a century from now. And the various possible technical solutions lie so far outside my ken that I am, perforce, required to turn my attention to the nearer future. There is only one remark I feel called upon to make with regard to these distant prospects. Technological advance may be expected not only to open up new sources of energy supply; it will inevitably create new and unexpected energy uses and new uses for energy materials. There is a demand as well as a supply factor in the energy equation. Consequently it is a mistake to think of the energy problem as exclusively one of meeting increasing requirements in current uses. We may be sure that as unconventional sources are developed unconventional requirements will also appear. The desalting of sea water is one that is clearly seen but there are others lying over the horizon.

We are concerned here, however, with the next two or at most three decades. Nineteen-eighty, give or take a year or two, is a date that may limit too frequent a resort to the crystal ball. It seems certain that within this period unconventional energy sources will supply only a small fraction of total energy requirements. A recent careful study projects nuclear energy at 10 per cent of the total United States

77

energy supply by 1980. [1] This seems to me on the high side but I am willing to accept it until more information is available. No doubt the percentage in various Western European countries will be somewhat higher than this though the cost figures from existing nuclear installations are somewhat discouraging and earlier construction plans have been drastically scaled down both in Britain and in the Euratom countries. In the underdeveloped world the rosy expectations of nuclear power expressed by various representatives at the Geneva Conference on Peaceful Uses of Atomic Energy in 1955 have since given way to soberer calculations. In reviewing this question I find no reason to change the opinion I expressed in a paper presented at that conference: that, largely because of the capital cost and foreign exchange requirements of atomic installations, the principal short-term expansion of these installations will be in the high-fuel-cost areas of the developed world rather than in underdeveloped areas however high their fuel costs. [2] Taking the free world as a whole then we may anticipate with some confidence that somewhat less than 10 per cent of total energy requirements will be met from nuclear sources by 1980.

This means that during the next two decades, so far as

[1] Perry D. Teitelbaum, *Productive Uses of Nuclear Energy* (National Planning Association, Washington, 1958).

[2] E. S. Mason and the National Planning Association Staff of the Peacetime Atomic Energy Project, "Energy Requirements and Economic Growth," in *Proceedings of the International Conference on Peaceful Uses of Atomic Energy*, Vol. I, p. 50. (United Nations, New York, 1956).

commercial sources are concerned, we shall continue to be dependent on hydro-power, coal, gas, and, primarily, oil. Indeed if I may anticipate in part a conclusion of this paper I would say that, if energy sources were free to move from low-cost locations in obedience to purely economic considerations the next two decades would belong to petroleum. Why energy sources will not in fact be free to move and the consequences thereof is the main part of my story.

Any respectable analysis of the energy outlook usually starts off with a projection of energy requirements. And it is remarkable in these days of linear programing, operations research, and input-output analysis how complicated the projections can become. For my purposes, however, this exercise seems unnecessary. I am willing to accept any one of a number of projections of energy consumption for the next twenty years, add or subtract 25 per cent and still maintain that if requirements can be met from lowest cost sources there is no reason to expect much, if any, rise in the cost per unit of energy input during the period under consideration. The great unknown in the analysis of future energy requirements is, of course, what will happen to rates of consumption in the underdeveloped world. During the last few decades, in the highly industrialized economies of the West, energy consumption has grown at slightly less than the rate of increase of real national income and most projections anticipate a continuation of this relationship. And we know that the determinants of growth in these economies are so firmly imbedded in existing habits and institutions that, barring large-scale warfare, we can project with

79

some confidence a growth trend in the future not very different from that experienced in the recent past. This, in fact, is the *differentia specifica* of a developed economy. In the underdeveloped world, however, we have no real basis for projecting growth rates and insufficient data to establish any firm relationship between growth rates and energy consumption. But it seems unlikely that energy requirements in this substantial part of the world will be large enough to change significantly our overall assessment.

One final preliminary observation concerns the relationship between low cost and abundance. It is obvious that for any particular source of energy—as indeed for any commodity—abundance cannot be assured without paying a price high enough not only to cover production or operating costs but also to cover any necessary expenses involved in assuring a continuing supply. This is a fact that is apparently not yet discovered in various Latin American countries who insist on setting electrical rates at a level so low that the replacement of existing installations becomes unprofitable. The same considerations have a bearing on domestic oil production. If we want to meet a large share of our energy requirements from domestic oil production we shall have to permit a price high enough to cover the increasing costs of discovery and development.

But what is true for particular sources of energy supply is substantially altered when we turn to an examination of all sources of energy considered together. Here low cost is compatible with abundance if first, there are, in fact, large supplies of low-cost energy available in the world and if, second, energy users are free to turn from high-cost to low-cost sources. Admittedly there are technical limitations to substitution among energy sources in particular uses and this is a fact of substantial importance for certain energy problems. But it is equally obvious that the possibilities of substitution are sufficiently great and that, if users are free to choose, energy prices will be lower in almost all uses.

A consideration of the relation of low cost and abundance also needs to take into account a missing intermediate factor, i.e., price. It is possible that, by any estimate of costs that is related to the inputs necessary to get a supply out of the ground and into the hands of users, a particular source of energy may be low cost. At the same time the price of energy from this source to the user may be high. This difference between the cost in terms of inputs and the delivered price per unit of output may be large because of high transport costs, because of the existence of monopoly elements in the market, or because the owner of the resource is in a position to exact a sizable rent or royalty, or for all these reasons. Since I presume we are here mainly concerned with low cost and abundance from the point of view of energy users it will be necessary to consider prices as well as input costs.

At this point I should logically plunge into an examination of the costs of alternative energy supplies in different parts of the world. This is at best a difficult task and for my purpose I consider it to be an unnecessary one. It is difficult to derive any accurate measures of the cost of producing, say, oil in different parts of the world for a number of reasons of which two are particularly important. First the very large differences in the security of investment in different parts of the world, mainly related to political considerations, suggest that very different periods of capital recovery are advisable. But making the most extreme allowances for these differences would still leave the Middle East and Venezuela remarkably low-cost sources of supply. Secondly, if one insists on charging to particular sources of supply the costs of exploration and discovery all over the world, one can build up a high-cost estimate even for Venezuela and the Middle East. There seems no very good reason for doing so but the problem of what exploration and development costs are to be charged to what sources of supply is admittedly a bothersome question.

It seems to me, however, that it is unnecessary for our purposes to enter into the intricacies of cost analysis. I take it for granted that Venezuela and the Middle East are low-cost sources on any full-cost-of-supply basis and the principal problem with respect to these areas that concerns users is the price problem. I believe it is clear that the costs of domestic oil in the United States are relatively high and may be rising. There seems to be ample evidence that coal can be produced in the United States at real costs no higher than at present for an indefinite period. On the other hand the facts indicate that coal costs in Western Europe are high and increasing. The situation with respect to gas production in the United States is less clear. Gas has been an extraordinary low-cost source of energy in this country and although the price in recent years has been rising rapidly

I am prepared to assume that it will continue to be a relatively low-cost source over the period we are considering. It is on the basis of these rough and ready approximations, that may be considered to be common knowledge, that I propose to proceed.

A realistic assessment of the prospects for low-cost and abundant energy in the Free World will, of necessity, have to grapple with the following questions:

1. Who, in fact, is interested in low-cost energy and what influence can they bring to bear, both in the market and in the political arena, as against the important groups who are certainly not interested in low prices, at least for their own outputs?

2. What changes in public policy and business practices would have to be brought about if we are to obtain a low-cost energy supply?

3. What would be the consequences of these changes for the economic position of particular sources of energy supply and for the defense posture of specific countries as seen by those responsible for security matters?

4. And finally, taking account of the probable answers to these questions, what role should low-cost, as against other considerations, play in the formulation of a sensible energy policy?

Turning to the first question it is abundantly clear that there are many groups, possessing great economic and political weight, who are not at all interested in a low-cost energy supply. If we look first at the domestic scene the gas producers, who are usually closely connected with oil production, complain bitterly that they are already selling at too low a price. They claim that their increasing share of the United States energy market is the result of an artificially determined differential; i.e., via government control of the field prices of gas, as against oil. They would like to be able to charge into the cost of gas the price of the oil that gas is displacing from the market. But if we consider any influence on price brought about by government intervention to be an "artificial" influence, gas is not the only energy source subject to such artificiality. Certainly, the domestic producers of oil, spread over twenty-two states each with its customary two senators, are not interested in low-cost energy. On the contrary they tend to assert that unless the price of oil is raised, or at least kept from declining, the increasing cost of domestic oil exploration and development will soon cease to be covered. The international oil companies, it is true, are interested in drawing a larger part of their oil, for sale in the United States, from lower cost foreign sources. But, so far as I know, they have not expressed a desire to pass these cost advantages on to consumers. Nor have I heard that John L. Lewis has spoken out in favor of a lower price for coal.

There are then some powerful market forces commanding significant political support which have no doubt an interest in abundant energy but not at low costs. Arrayed against them are some special groups of whom the twelve New England Senators, chivied by a constituency interested in low residual fuel oil prices, are perhaps the most vocal. For the rest the interest in low energy cost is a diffuse consumer interest which like all consumer manifestations is disorganized and relatively impotent.

The situation in Western Europe is not too dissimilar. Although oil from the Middle East can now be landed in most of Western Europe at prices which tend to make the high-cost domestic coal output noncompetitive, strong forces are arrayed against a rapid displacement. In Germany the favored method is a differential tax on oil consumption. In Belgium despite all the efforts of the European Coal and Steel Community to close down high-cost mines there is effective resistance. In Britain the government stands ready by differential taxes on oil and, if necessary, by subsidies to coal, to protect this high-cost, and also high-employment, source of energy supply.

As our attention turns to the principal centers of overseas oil production, Venezuela and the Middle East, we find, quite naturally, no very great enthusiasm for low-cost energy. There is, it is true, a great desire to see a lowering of barriers to oil imports in the West. This in itself would tend to lower the average costs of energy inputs in Europe and arrest a tendency toward increasing energy costs in the future in the United States. But neither the producing companies nor the owning governments are interested in any substantial break in the world price structure. The tremendous surplus now overhanging the market and the entrance over the last few years of new producing interests has, it is true, induced a substantial nibbling at this price structure.

But it remains to be seen whether such price-lowering influences as may be brought to bear by increasing competition and overabundant supplies may not be offset by the effects of increasing pressure by owning governments for a larger share in the proceeds.

No doubt if we pushed our search for consuming interests concerned with low-cost energy very far into the underdeveloped world we would find countries whose import needs and shortage of foreign exchange makes this concern a matter of critical importance. But the influence of these countries on world energy prices is not apt to be large. Taking the free world as a whole we must conclude that the forces arrayed against the objective of a low-cost energy supply are strong.

Let us consider now what changes in public policy and business practices would have to be accomplished if we are to obtain a low-cost and abundant energy supply. Undoubtedly a necessary, if not sufficient, condition is a lowering or elimination of import barriers to—and differential taxation of—oil in Western Europe and the United States. In this country an elimination of import barriers would inevitably produce a large influx of oil whether or not the delivered price was affected. International companies free to choose between their high-cost domestic and their low-cost foreign sources would have no doubts concerning the correct procedure. Independents who have been going abroad in increasing numbers in recent years but who have encountered difficulties in disposing of their oil in the American market would have their difficulties lessened. And other independents would join the race to Venezuela and the Middle East.

In Western Europe if import barriers were removed *and* if differential taxes on petroleum and subsidies to coal were also lessened or eliminated, oil would replace coal at a greatly accelerated rate. Here, as I have indicated, such a replacement would lower the average costs of energy inputs even if the price of oil remained constant. In the United States it would probably not have this effect since coal prices are fairly competitive with oil in common uses and gas is still an exceptionally low-cost alternative source of energy. Expansion of imports, however, might well postpone any increase in United States energy prices.

Assuming the price of imported oil were to remain constant such a pronounced shift in energy sources would still inevitably lower the cost of supplying world energy requirements in terms of real inputs and this is an element not to be ignored. Instead of the labor and capital required in the United States to find oil in increasingly unlikely territory or to undertake increasingly difficult secondary recovery operations, the much smaller physical inputs needed to produce oil in Venezuela or the Middle East would be called on. And in Western Europe the very heavy labor and capital investment per ton of coal would no longer be needed. Needless to say this view is a reflexion of the Free World energy potential seen as a whole. For any particular country the real cost of imported oil is dependent on the real costs of the exports that pay for these imports. Furthermore even for the Free World as a whole the saving in a shift from high input sources to low import sources is real only if the displaced resources can be effectively reemployed. Despite these caveats, a potential Free World saving of inputs is an aspect of the matter that needs to be considered.

When we ask ourselves what changes in public policies or business practices, in addition to a freeing of imports, would be needed to lower energy prices to consumers, we run into a hornets' nest of unanswered, and probably unanswerable, speculations. Clearly the crux of the matter is how and whether the f.o.b. price of oil at the really rich oil-producing centers can be brought somewhat closer to input costs? This involves among other things speculation on the future competitive structure of the producing industry particularly in these areas, the bargaining position of the various owning country governments vis-à-vis the producing companies with respect to sharing profits and various consumer country governments with respect to price. And, since the capital requirements of a greatly expanded overseas oil supply are very large, the attitude of potential investors toward these developments is decidedly relevant. One really needs to dust off the crystal ball to provide answers.

The impinging forces are contradictory to say the least. An expansion of the market for Middle Eastern and Venezuelan oil would tend to bring in a flock of new producers and thus might lessen the influence of individual major companies on the price structure. But such an influx would tend to strengthen the hand of the owning countries and possibly their share of the take. On the other hand the vastness of the overhang surplus oil plus new discoveries like those in Algeria and Libya may substantially weaken this bargaining power. If these elements together with the possibilities of collusive arrangements among the owning or the consuming countries are taken into account we seem to have a situation in which you pick your number and take your choice.

One final remark on this question. I have discussed the issue entirely in terms of oil because I believe that the center of the question of what happens to world energy prices over the next two decades lies in what happens to the geographical distribution and to the f.o.b. price of oil from the really low-cost areas with their superabundant reserves.

A consideration of the probable consequences of shifts of this sort for the economic position of particular groups of producers and for the defense posture of individual countries can be brief. The probable economic consequences are fairly obvious and fairly drastic. The security considerations belong much more to the province of our next speaker. An elimination of barriers to oil imports into the United States would bear most heavily on domestic oil producers. Such a displacement would cut back allowables—already reduced to nine days a month in Texas—to a point where the continuation of proration and all that it involves in the way of output controls, might well have to be reconsidered. If output controls were substantially altered both the domestic and import price would fall, a good many marginal operations would be abandoned and no doubt expenditures on exploration and development would be sharply reduced.

If the displacement of domestic by foreign output took place without a substantial change in the delivered price of oil there is no reason to suppose that the production and consumption trends of coal or gas would be so affected. On the other hand if increased oil imports led to a reconsideration of domestic output controls and price competition raised its ugly head this judgment would have to be re-examined.

An abandonment of import barriers to and differential taxation on oil in Western Europe would produce rapid inroads into coal production and, what is probably more important, into the heavy employment in the coal industries of various European countries. In contrast to the United States where only 200,000 men are currently employed in coal production, Britain employs some 750,000 to produce slightly more than one-half the United States output, and West Germany some 450,000.

In view of the probable impact in the United States and Western Europe of an abandonment of competitive restrictions on foreign oil—which I regard as the necessary if not sufficient condition to low-cost and abundant energy during the next two decades—the question naturally arises, how much do we want a low-cost energy supply? But before attempting to assess the relative importance of lowness of cost in a sensible energy policy let me call attention to certain economic aspects of the security problem.

An economist viewing developments of the last few years cannot help wondering whether, in the event of nuclear warfare, energy-consuming facilities will not disappear at least as rapidly as energy-producing facilities. Is it then so important to build up a supply cushion in the United States particularly if the cost of so doing is very high? He cannot help wondering also whether, in the event of brush-fire wars of various sorts, energy sources outside the United States may not be as useful as those inside. Finally, looking at the experience of the last war, one wonders whether rationing is not a quicker and more productive source of energy for military use than the creation of surplus capacity. Abandonment of import controls will certainly make us more dependent on foreign sources of supply. But does this necessarily make us any more vulnerable to the dangers that now confront us?

Let us turn now to the final question. I have been somewhat amused recently to note a request from a high authority in the European Community for a brief description of United States energy policy. This exhibits a touching faith in the rationality of public action in the United States but no great awareness of how things, in fact, get done. So far as I am aware the United States has no energy policy and despite recent emanations from Congress on this matter I doubt whether we will soon have one. If, however, we can imagine a sensible energy policy what role would low-cost considerations play as against the legitimate interests of domestic producing groups and as against security consideration?

This is much too large a hare to start at this stage. But a concluding remark needs to be made concerning the role of costs in such a calculus. Until recently the United States enjoyed a pronounced advantage over every other country in the world with respect to energy costs. The richness and accessibility of our coal deposits were, and still are, unmatched in other industrial countries. The United States was the principal exporter of oil and oil products, and oil prices in the rest of the world were U.S. Gulf prices plus delivery costs to destination. And we were the first large consumer of gas.

Energy prices are still comparatively low in this country but we have already lost a substantial part of our advantage. The delivered price of crude oil is now somewhat lower in the highly industrialized sections of the Western Europe than it is in the highly industrialized sections of the United States. Furthermore, an energy policy in this country which emphasized the interests of domestic producing groups and defense considerations at the expense of the cost element would soon reverse our traditional position. While the effects of low-cost energy on economic growth in the United States can be exaggerated, a transition from relatively low-cost to relatively high-cost energy inputs would quite definitely weaken our competitive position in the world. In a period when this position is already beginning to appear precarious I do not believe that an energy policy which fails to put cost considerations in the front rank can, by any stretch of the imagination, be called sensible.

DEAN BROWN: Thank you, Professor Mason. That was a most perceptive analysis of the pros and cons of policies that would lead to or away from abundant and low-cost supplies of energy. There was one thing, Professor Mason, that you did not touch on, which I would like to ask a question about, and that is the relationship of the overall increment of demand for energy to this problem, which, I take it, would be a function of whether we pursue one course or the other. Would you wish to comment on the rate of increase in the demand for energy during the next two decades, relative to that of the past decades?

Dr. Mason: I had a section on energy projections in this paper, but it was already overlong, so I cut it out in my verbal remarks. What I would like to say is something like this, that as far as the United States is concerned and as far as most Western European countries are concerned, the indications from the last few decades are that the rate of increase in overall energy requirements is slightly less than the rate of increase in real national product.

That is, in the United States, if the real national product is increasing at 3½ per cent per annum, it looks as though our rate of increase in energy requirements would be slightly less than that, and it looks as though something like that relationship exists in the Western European countries also, and that kind of a relationship, as a matter of fact, is used in most of the energy projections that I have seen.

Now, when you turn to the underdeveloped world, of course you have a totally unknown situation. In the first place, you don't know whether these countries are going to grow, you don't know what the rate of increase in national income is likely to be, if any, and secondly, you have no statistical information that permits you to establish any kind of relationship between changes and growth in national income and energy requirements.

DEAN BROWN: As Professor Mason has pointed out, these last two papers do overlap to a certain extent necessarily. So I think it wise to proceed to our next speaker, and then let the audience direct their questions at either Professor Mason or Mr. Hoover.

V. ENERGY AND PUBLIC AFFAIRS

by Herbert Hoover, Jr.

It is an honor to participate in this centennial celebration of the founding of the petroleum industry. Oil has become one of our greatest sources of energy—and with it has come a revolution in American life.

When Drake completed his well, just a short distance from here, he could not possibly have guessed at the forces he was setting in motion, or at the events which would follow. He could not have dreamed that a hundred years later oil and gas would be providing almost three-quarters of all the energy consumed in the United States.

In his time, Drake was engaged in a private, speculative business venture that was of little concern to anyone beyond the limited circle of people who were associated with him. Certainly it would never have occurred to him that a century later a discussion on Energy and Man, such as we are now engaged in, would be provoked by his discovery. The fact is, however, that petroleum has become so vital to human welfare everywhere that its availability is a matter of deepest concern to people and governments the world over.

97

America's industrial life has been dependent on an abundance of low-cost energy. The existence within our borders of virtually unlimited reserves of coal was the foundation of this abundance. But it has been the abundance of petroleum and natural gas that has been responsible for the more recent dramatic growth of our standard of living and our comfort.

Ownership of the Subsoil

One of the fundamental differences that has developed in the growth pattern of energy around the world has involved ownership of the subsoil rights.

The early development of the coal and petroleum industries in the United States was predicated on the concept that the landowner held title to the underlying minerals. This philosophy has continued, with the result that the application of statutory and legal processes has affected, with reasonable impartiality, both landowner and producer. Governmental action or politics has not entered into this aspect of the energy picture.

In many foreign countries, however, the state owns the resources *in situ*. It has either produced them as a government enterprise or leased them under some form of contractual agreement. In either event, the production of energy has become inextricably bound up on the processes of government—and in public affairs.

In our own country, notwithstanding the vital importance of energy to the public welfare, it is interesting that there have been relatively few instances where regulations were imposed that did not apply to industry in general. The reason, no doubt, has been the wide availability of these resources. Some regulations have made a great contribution to the abundance and usefulness of energy in our American society. Others, perhaps, have done less so.

This is such a broad and ramified subject that, for the purpose of this discussion, I propose to take a few specific examples of the more important types of regulation to show how far-reaching, in some instances, has been the impact of public affairs upon the availability and cost of energy.

Competition

The maintenance of competition through antitrust legislation, for example, has been one of the basic and necessary concepts of our American free-enterprise system. Without doubt, the overall effect of this Federal regulation has been on the plus side of the ledger. Under the spur of competition the fuel industries, in particular, have become among the most progressive, efficient, and competently managed segments of the American economy. They have provided energy at lower relative cost to the consumer than in any other industrialized country in the world.

State Regulation of Production

A different type of governmental action—and one of the few that has pertained specifically to the energy industry—has been the regulation of crude oil production by some of the petroleum-producing states. This development, dating from the 1920's, has had a vital bearing on the long-term

99

availability of domestic energy sources through the conservation of crude oil reserves.

Before state regulation was instituted, periods of overproduction lowered reservoir pressures prematurely, and the ultimate recovery of oil was drastically reduced. Prices often reacted violently to relatively small variations in supply or demand, and a boom-or-bust psychology created waste, inefficiency, and financial instability.

Methods used by state commissions, especially in Texas, have contributed substantially to the conservation of petroleum resources. They have also brought about a larger measure of stability to the industry; efficiency has improved, and great technological progress has taken place.

There is ample room for still further progress if these efforts can be maintained. Present methods of production can recover only about 30 per cent of the original crude oil in place, and reserve figures are predicated on that basis. Even a slight improvement in producing techniques, therefore, could add substantially to our overall reserves.

One of the practical effects of state regulation has been to make possible an expansion of production for emergencies of between two and three million barrels per day. On the other hand, the higher figure probably could not be sustained for any appreciable length of time without affecting ultimate recovery. A lower estimate would be more realistic. The Suez emergency indicated that even an increase of one million barrels per day was not possible to sustain in practice because of lack of pipeline facilities.

Regardless of the reason, if a potential reserve is to be

useful, the facilities must exist before the emergency arises, and some form of incentive to the industry would seem to be justified. (In the Suez incident it is doubtful if the shortages in Europe could have been met had it not been for an unanticipated increase of production from South America.)

Natural Gas

Another and more recent area where governmental action has had an impact on domestic sources of energy has been in the field of natural gas. Here is one of the few instances, if not the only one, where the Federal Government is exercising direct regulation of fuel prices at the source of production under peacetime conditions.

This action was not the result of direct legislation, but took place through a chain of legal circumstances, culminating in the Phillips decision of the United States Supreme Court in 1954. Without entering into the legal details of the case, it is sufficient to point out some of the economic consequences to the overall energy situation.

Until recent years, natural gas was essentially a surplus by-product of crude oil production. At the time regulatory action began, prices were on the order of 10 cents per MCF, or less, at the well head. On a BTU basis, this was equivalent to something less than 60 cents per barrel, compared to the average prevailing crude price of about $3.00 per barrel. The effect of perpetuating this abnormally low price for gas has stimulated its use at the expense of other fuels—especially oil. If exploration and production of oil and gas

101

are regarded as a joint-cost operation, as they certainly are, then gas is far from carrying its share of the cost at such price levels. The result has been a substantial lessening of the incentive to develop new reserves, both of gas and oil.

The impact of gas on the overall use of petroleum energy is shown by the consumption figures over the last ten years. Expressed on an equivalent fuel basis, from 1948 to 1958 gas (including gas liquids) increased from 2.9 million B/D to 6.2 million B/D, or 115 per cent, while domestic crude oil production increased from 5.5 million B/D to 6.7 million B/D, or 22 per cent. If these trends of growth continue, gas, the former by-product, may well become the largest single domestic source of energy.

The maintenance of an artificially low price for gas also has had a depressing effect on coal which, until recent years, consistently contributed a third or more of our domestic energy requirements. While extremely large domestic reserves of coal are theoretically available, the practical effect is to cause a premature abandonment of mines and other facilities which, once closed, cannot be economically revived except under conditions of abnormally high prices. The drifting away of skilled workers into other occupations is equally serious in its long-term aspects.

While the short-term effect of this political action has been to provide energy at lower cost and in greater volume, the depressing effect on oil and coal production—together with the reduced incentives to locate additional reserves of oil and gas—may well prove to be anything but helpful in maintaining long-term abundance.

The free play of economic forces in determining the competitive fuel pattern would eventually dictate the optimum use of natural gas, and would minimize its use in uneconomic ways.

Government versus Private Operation

Little need be said here about direct government operation of oil production that has not already been stated elsewhere many times before. It is perhaps pertinent to note, however, that countries which have pursued the philosophy of nationalized operation, excluding the Communist bloc, are estimated to possess less than 2 per cent of the Free World's discovered reserves of oil. In each instance the decision to undertake government operation was political rather than economic.

By contrast, the countries where energy resources are owned by the state, but operated under some form of contractual agreement, possess almost 90 per cent of the Free World's proven petroleum reserves. The nations in which these major reserves occur, with few exceptions, are in the so-called less developed category. In most instances, their petroleum resources, actual or potential, are overwhelming in size compared to their other economic assets, and their hopes and aspirations for economic and social improvement revolve largely around the expansion of petroleum production.

From the political standpoint, there are a number of practical consequences. These governments naturally want maximum possible revenues, employment, and other bene-

103

fits. It is also a matter of national pride that their share of income shall be no less than that of other producing countries. In such a setting, the appeal of nationalism can cause strong emotional responses in public opinion. Under such pressures, it is understandable that governments may find it difficult to carry out their contractual agreements. The chances of friction and misunderstanding—or even an impasse—are considerable. Organized Communist agitation often compounds the difficulties.

The cost of energy from foreign sources has tended to rise steadily, not only because of pressure for larger government royalties or taxes, but also because of the higher costs of operation incident to the improvement of their economies. On the average, however, costs are still somewhat lower than those in older areas, primarily because of the prolific nature of their oil fields.

Within the last three years, discoveries have been made in several new areas abroad which give promise of providing very large reserves. Other countries, where only moderate quantities have been found so far, could conceivably fulfill their own requirements or even develop a surplus for export. This may well bring about a more sobering perspective on the part of all governments in their international dealings.

On the whole, the wide geographic distribution of these new reserves should be a helpful factor in promoting peaceful progress. The fact remains, however, that there is a vast potential oversupply of petroleum energy available in the world today, and, barring some unexpected emergency, this will continue for many years to come.

Petroleum Imports

The most recent instance of governmental action affecting the domestic supply of energy has been Federal limitation of petroleum imports.

Until ten years ago, the United States supplied all of its own petroleum requirements and even had a surplus for export. Beginning about 1947, conditions changed, although the effects were obscured and delayed by a series of events, including the war in Korea, the shutdown of production in Iran, and the closing of the Suez Canal and the Syrian pipelines.

Since 1947, costs of exploration and production have risen sharply in the United States due to substantial increases in wages and materials. At the same time discovery rates have increased abroad, and a large potential volume of low-cost production, substantially in excess of world demand, has been developed.

The American situation became acute in 1957 when the Suez Canal and the pipelines returned to normal operation. Estimates of imports for the last half of 1957, when added to normal domestic production, were far in excess of domestic demand.

Under the authority of the Trade Agreements Act, a voluntary system of import limitation was adopted by the Federal Government in 1957. Subsequently, in the early part of 1959, a mandatory system was placed in effect. It is too early to determine whether the present method of control will prove to be the most desirable one, or whether some alternative may be more suitable. The administrative problem is not so much one of determining the total volume of imports as it is to choose a method of apportioning the imports among individual elements of the industry. Regardless of this difficulty, it seems certain that some form of limitation will continue for the foreseeable future.

In setting forth the reasons for import controls in 1957, the President's Cabinet Committee summarized the situation as follows:

> Unless a reasonable limitation of petroleum imports is brought about, your committee believes that:
> (1) Oil imports will flow into this country in ever-mounting quantities, entirely disproportionate to the quantities needed to supplement domestic supply.
> (2) There will be a resultant discouragement of and decrease in, domestic production.
> (3) There will be a marked decline in domestic exploration and development.
> (4) In the event of a serious emergency, this nation will find itself years away from attaining the level of petroleum production necessary to meet our national security needs.

In basing its recommendations on the grounds of national security, the committee was of course guided by broad considerations of the national interest and safety, rather than by the more narrow requirements of military logistics.

From a purely military standpoint, a discussion of energy resources often becomes lost in arguments as to whether another emergency would become a global, short, and immediately devastating general war; or a situation of more limited and prolonged character. We pray fervently that neither will happen, but it is well to remember that two of the major emergencies that have actually taken place in the last fifteen years—Korea and Suez—required rapid and full-scale mobilization of the Free World's energy resources.

In view of the kind of world we are living in, it would seem prudent to be prepared for either alternative, and leave no room for miscalculation by those who might be tempted to indulge in it.

From the broad standpoint of national security, the ultimate success of this or any other method of limiting petroleum imports lies in the results to be achieved. It will be several years before a judgment can be reached because of the appreciable time lag between initial exploration and the final availability of proven resources. Moreover, there are other economic crosscurrents, such as the natural gas situation, that preclude arriving at an immediate conclusion.

There seems to be general agreement, however, that adequate prospects for new fields are still available, and that given reasonable incentives to find them, ample domestic reserves can be developed and maintained for the foreseeable future. The necessity of continuing governmental policies to provide such incentives is of the utmost importance.

Over a period of nearly two centuries in our national existence, one of our strongest assets in working toward peaceful and constructive solutions to many of the world's problems has been our independence in one of our most vital resources—energy.

It is of paramount importance to our nation's security that we maintain this independence. Under the circumstances of the foreseeable future, I believe we can do so without excessive cost and without impairing abundant availabilities.

In concluding this symposium I would like to touch briefly upon one additional aspect of the energy-resource picture—the human element. While it may seem far removed from this discussion, which has been centered largely on governmental regulation and economics, it is in many ways one of the most fundamental problems of all.

Ever since Drake brought in his first oil well, the human element has been an indispensable ingredient in providing our country with an abundance of low-cost energy. True, the natural resources were there from the beginning. But it was the adventuresome and enterprising spirit of the people in the energy industries, from top to bottom, that made these resources available and converted them into useful form. They had the same pioneering spirit that pushed the early settlers westward across the mountains and prairies to make America great. It is a spirit that has remained as a heritage in the mining and petroleum industries ever since.

One of the impelling forces behind this spirit has been the incentive to take risks and to get the job done. Difficulties, whether physical or technical, became a challenge rather than a barrier.

If this spirit is lost, either through eroding away the incentives or by undue regulation, then we may have real concern for the years to come. If it can be maintained, we can look to the future with confidence that abundant, low-cost energy will be available to fulfill the vital needs of our national life.

DEAN BROWN: Thank you, Mr. Hoover.

In this final discussion the audience may address questions to either Professor Mason or Mr. Hoover or to both, and they will be directed as you wish.

I have one that was asked of Professor Mason, but since it is so pertinent to some of the comments that Mr. Hoover made, I will direct it to him. In view of the statement that gas will continue as a low-cost energy supply, may it be inferred that the current price is adequate to encourage the finding and development of the required gas supply?

MR. HOOVER: Well, I'm a little hesitant to embark on that subject in the presence of members of the Federal Power Commission, as I am sure that any one of them here could do a much better job of answering the question than I could possibly myself.

To repeat what I said very briefly in my text, gas was a surplus by-product of oil. In the early days of the industry, it was blown off into the atmosphere as sheer waste because it couldn't be used at all. Therefore, its price started at one or two cents a thousand, but crept up gradually.

Because of increasing demand it reached a point of approximately 10 cents a thousand and was continuing to creep up slowly at the time regulation of gas prices began, and essentially the price has remained more or less the same since. This price is, of course, far below that for equivalent fuel value contained in either petroleum or coal, and demand at that low price has expanded enormously, as the figures I quoted show.

DEAN BROWN: The next question is addressed to Dr. Mason. Can you cite an example of government regulation or control that refutes the principle that, in the regulation of commercial activity, the government can only create a shortage?

DR. MASON: Certainly, the Texas Railway Commission is an example of government creating a shortage. I don't know exactly what the bearing of this question is, but let me say a few words about this.

I listened with some interest this morning to Mr. Dunlop saying that the oil industry flourishes best in an atmosphere of no government interference. Now, no government interference to me would mean abolition of the proration system, putting the Texas Railway Commission out of business, eliminating tariffs on imports—I'm just a simple academic economist, but to me, a free market without government intervention implies something like that.

I think that the oil industry really doesn't want exactly free market conditions in the production of petroleum. Obviously, the intervention of the government has disadvantages to industry in many ways. Mr. Dunlop mentioned this morning the very high tax on gasoline in the United States.

If ever the government, in an attempt to formulate an energy policy, posed end-use controls, reserving, let us say, coal to a certain part of the market, that obviously would be a very damaging action with respect to the petroleum industry. The government acts in certain ways which are disadvantageous, but I would say that it also certainly acts in this country in ways that are advantageous.

DEAN BROWN: I have another question for you while you are there. Dr. Mason, you seem to admit great competition in the oil industry, but yet doubt whether prices will be very low. Does this imply less correlation between competition and prices than is found in the traditional view of economics?

DR. MASON: I think that's a rather complicated question to answer. Suppose, for example, you were talking about oil from Venezuela or the Middle East. What would be the effect of the entrance of a large number of new independent firms into those areas?

I'm not at all sure that price would be reduced because I don't know what the behavior of the Venezuelan government or the various states in the Middle East would be with respect to the share of the take they demand. There are so many other things in addition to competition that affect the price of oil, that it would be difficult to separate out this particular element.

Ordinarily, of course, an economist would say that if the intensity of competition is increased, it will probably have

111

some effect on the price. It would lower the price, unless the price was already so low that it was no more than sufficient to cover the costs of sustaining a volume of output.

DEAN BROWN: Mr. Hoover, would not the imposition of an *adequate* tariff on foreign oil be more effective than controlling imports (I presume this means more effective than quotas) and would it not also preserve necessary incentives for the domestic industry?

MR. HOOVER: That is probably one of the most complicated subjects in the whole import problem. If it was simply a matter of tariff against some form of limitation in terms of a quota, it would be easier, but it is far more complicated than that.

On the one hand, the impact of tariffs on our foreign relations is extraordinarily serious. Without changing the price, perhaps, in the domestic market, a tariff has the effect, in many cases, of pushing the price down in the producing country to the extent of the tariff. On the other hand, there is no question that a tariff leads less to a regimented industry than do methods such as quotas or various physical import controls.

Another problem is that, theoretically at least, a tariff is applied supposedly to equalize differences in the cost of production. Well, unfortunately there is no single country in the world that has a nice average cost of petroleum. Some are high and some are low, and you get into a perfectly impossible situation trying to assess a tariff of different sizes on different countries. You would be making first, second, third, and fourth class citizens out of all of our friends abroad, and they undoubtedly would be even madder about that than about the tariff itself.

DEAN BROWN: We have imposed on our panelists and on the people in the audience for a long day. I think we had better pass further questions now, and I would like to ask Mr. Porter to close the session.

MR. PORTER: I want to repeat what I said at the start, and that is, it has been a great opportunity for the American Petroleum Institute and the petroleum industry to co-sponsor this symposium. I don't believe, and I am sure you all agree with me, that I have ever had an opportunity of hearing in one day as fine a group of speakers as we have had here. So I want to thank you, Dean Brown, for this opportunity. I know you have been largely responsible for all the arrangements. I don't know whether we can have one of these symposia every year or not, but I think we should every so often. It would be most interesting and helpful, not only to the people in our industry, but to people at large.

Thank you very much, gentlemen, for being here. I hope you agree that this has been a very eventful, fruitful day.

Date Due

MAR 1 1974		
MAR 16 1974		
APR 2 1975		
DEC 8 '76		
MAR 30 '77		
JUL 1 '77		
APR 5 '78		
OCT 27 '78		
JUL 3 '79		
AUG 1 3 1983